Traditional Tales

Paul Johnson

A & C Black • London

Reprinted 2005

First published 2002 by A & C Black Publishers Ltd
37 Soho Square, London W1D 3QZ

www.acblack.com

ISBN 0-7136-6234-4

Copyright project ideas © Paul Johnson, 2002
Copyright illustrations © Kirsty Wilson, 2002
Copyright cover illustration © Alex Ayliffe, 2002
Teachers' notes and stories retold by Christine Moorcroft
Editor: Lucy Poddington

A CIP catalogue record for this book is available from the
British Library.

A & C Black uses paper produced with elemental chlorine-free pulp,
harvested from managed, sustainable forests.
Printed in Great Britain by Caligraving Ltd, Thetford, Norfolk.

Contents

Introduction

How to use this book

Copy and Cut: Traditional Tales provides a variety of photocopiable craft templates, each with simple instructions for children to follow. The templates enable children to make storybooks and models based on the stories, themes and characters of well-known traditional tales. The projects provide innovative contexts for practising writing and literacy skills. There are opportunities for the children to read instructions and write text for a purpose, including stories, lists and playscripts.

The projects are designed for six to eight year-olds, but many are also suitable for younger children. Any project can be easily adapted to your needs by masking and/or substituting text. Favourite templates can be removed from the book and filed with other relevant resources. At the back of the book, you will find photocopiable story texts of less well-known tales for children to read and use for their own storybooks. There are notes for teachers which include practical suggestions and additional information on the featured stories.

Preparation

First pull out the template page and cut around the border. Use this master page for all future photocopying. (For a more exact copy, lay the page on the photocopier plate rather than feeding it in.) To begin a project, photocopy both sides of the template for each child and check that the necessary resources are available (see 'You will need' for individual projects). Introduce the theme and discuss ideas for the project with the whole class. If necessary, read the instructions with the children and demonstrate what they mean. It is particularly useful to show the children how to hold the page to start with. A photocopiable page of helpful hints is provided on page 60.

Decorating the projects

The templates can be reproduced on white or coloured paper or card, either as A4 or enlarged to A3. A3 is a particularly useful size for demonstration purposes and storybooks. The instructions suggest basic decorating materials such as coloured pencils, to avoid requests for materials that may not be available. However, it would be useful to start a collection of extra resources,

so that children can be more adventurous with their decorations. Suitable materials include glitter glue, pearlised paints, metallic pens and paper, coloured foil paper, sequin mesh, tinsel, holographic paper, art straws, sweet papers, wrapping paper, magazines, fabric and wool.

Tips for good results

Encourage the children to try out decoration ideas on an odd piece of paper first, and to plan in pencil. It's a good idea to avoid the use of fibre-tipped pens, as colours may run through the paper. If you copy the template on to card, show the children how to score along the dots with a pencil and ruler before folding.

You could consider making two copies of the template for each pupil. One can be used for the rough draft and the other for the finished piece. For the storybook projects, the children may find it helpful to write a first draft of the text on a plain sheet of paper, then to edit their writing before writing the final version in their book. Alternatively, they could word-process texts and stick them on to their finished card or book.

Ideas for display

These projects are perfect for school displays. Why not mount projects together on a classroom wall or in the school hall?

Anansi character tree

Anansi the spider loves bananas! Read the story and think about the characters of Anansi and the Banana Bird. Then write about each character on your tree.

You will need: the Anansi character tree template • the story of Anansi and the Banana Bird • scissors • pencil • pencil crayons for decorating

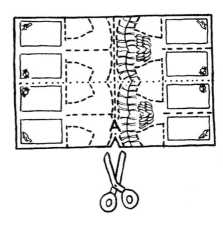

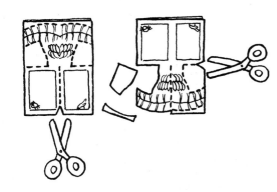

1. Cut the paper in half along the A dashes.

2. Fold each piece of paper in half along the B dots.

3. Cut along all the dashes on each piece of paper.

4. Slot together the two pieces of paper, like this. Now stand your tree up.

Press your tree flat so that you can write on it. Think of words that describe what Anansi the spider is like. Write a sentence about Anansi on each page with a spider on it.

Now think about what the Banana Bird is like. On each page with a bird on it, write a sentence about the Banana Bird. Decorate your model using coloured pencils.

Anansi is clever and witty.

The Blue Jackal

The Blue Jackal is a story from India. In the story, a nosy jackal has an accident and turns himself blue! Tell the story yourself on this model.
Talk about the moral with a friend.

You will need: the Blue Jackal template • the story of The Blue Jackal • scissors • pencil • pencil crayons for decorating

1. Fold the paper in half widthways, like this.

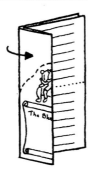

2. Fold forwards along the A dots. Then fold backwards. Unfold along the A dots.

3. Cut along the dashes.

4. Open out the paper. Fold along the B dots, like this.

5. Stand up your model and pull the jackal forwards.

Read the story and make notes about what happens on a separate piece of paper. Press your model flat and write the story in your own words. Continue on the back and write the moral at the end. Colour the picture of the jackal. Under the heading, you could write some of the rules the jackal makes.

The Blue Jackal

Moral

Two Heads are Better than One

No one has two heads! So what does the title of this story mean? Read the story and talk to a friend about its message. Then make this book. Write in the speech bubbles to tell the story.

You will need: the Two Heads are Better than One template • the story of Two Heads are Better than One • scissors • pencil • pencil crayons for decorating

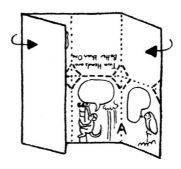

1. Fold the paper forwards along all the A dots. Unfold.

2. Fold the paper in half lengthways, like this. Unfold.

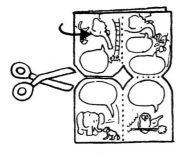

3. Fold the paper in half widthways, like this. Cut along all the dashes.

4. Open out the paper. Fold in half lengthways again.

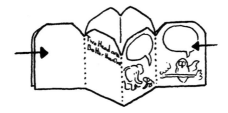

5. Push the left and right edges towards each other, to make a box shape in the middle. Keep pushing until the sides touch.

6. Fold the cover around all the other pages.

Read the story. Then look at the pictures in your book. Read the story again and decide what to write in each speech bubble. Draw a picture on the front cover. Write the moral of the story on the back cover.

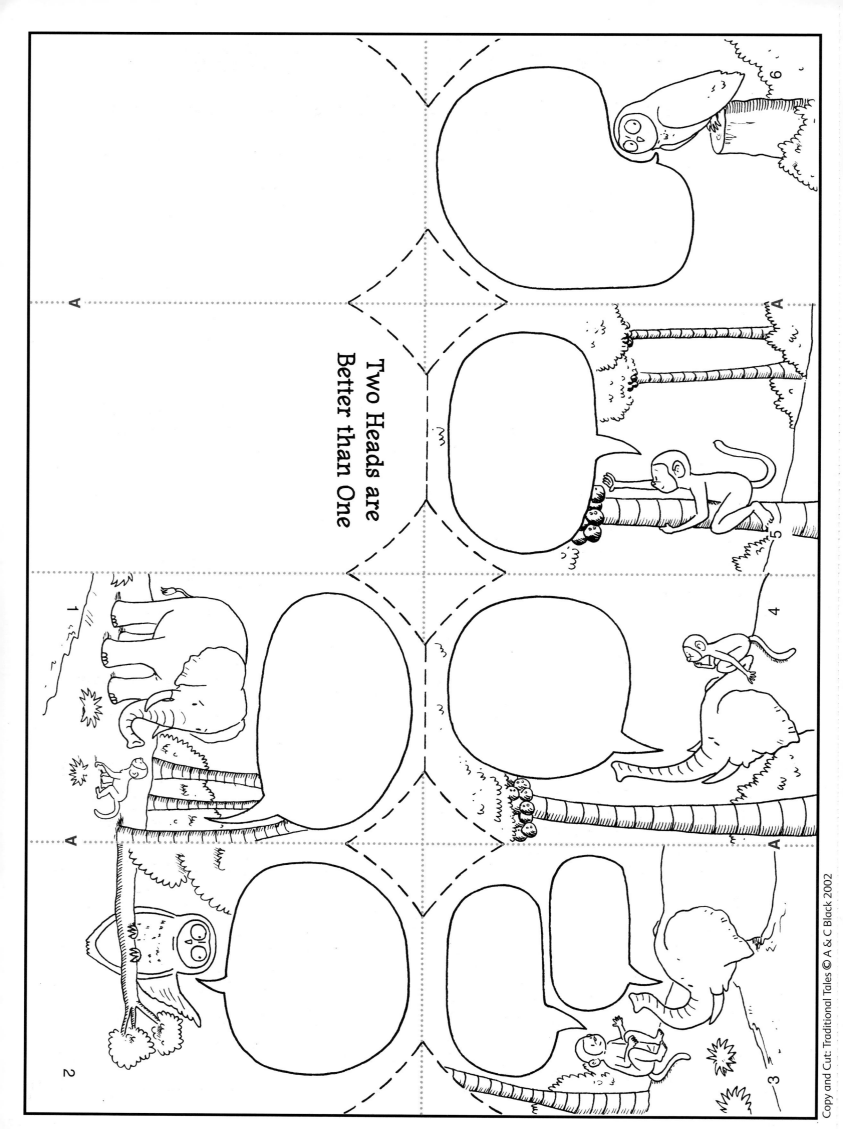

Two Heads are Better than One

Three wishes book

In the tale of Aladdin, a genie popped out of the magic lamp! He made Aladdin's wishes come true. If you could have three wishes, what would they be? Write and draw them in this book.

You will need: the Three wishes book template • scissors • glue • pencil • pencil crayons for decorating

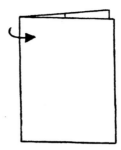

1. Fold the paper in half widthways, like this. Unfold.

2. With the blank side facing you, fold forwards along all the A dots and dashes. Unfold.

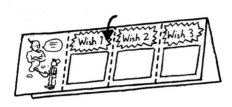

3. Fold the paper in half lengthways, like this. Unfold.

4. Cut along all the dashes.

5. Fold the paper in half lengthways again. Lift up the Aladdin picture and spread glue on the inside.

6. Fold the page back down. Fold the book in a zig-zag and press down firmly.

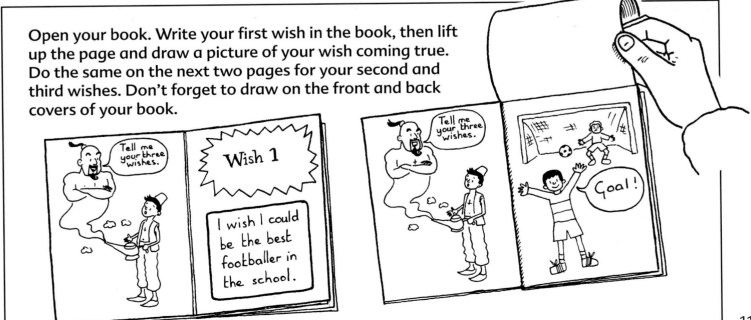

Open your book. Write your first wish in the book, then lift up the page and draw a picture of your wish coming true. Do the same on the next two pages for your second and third wishes. Don't forget to draw on the front and back covers of your book.

Tell me your three wishes.

Three wishes book

Wish 1

Wish 2

Wish 3

The Emperor and the Nightingale

This story is about an emperor who ruled China many years ago. He loved to listen to a nightingale singing. Tell the story yourself in this book. Draw pictures to show what happens.

You will need: the Emperor and the Nightingale template • the story of The Emperor and the Nightingale • scissors • pencil • pencil crayons for decorating

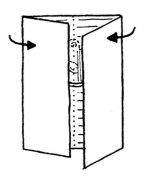

1. Fold the paper forwards along all the A dots. Unfold.

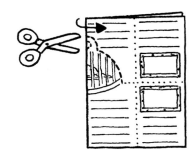

2. Fold the paper in half widthways, like this. Cut along all the dashes. Unfold.

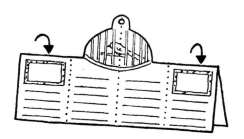

3. Fold the paper along all the B dots.

4. Fold your book in a zig-zag to close it.

Read the story of The Emperor and the Nightingale. Then write the story in your own words in your book. Draw pictures in the boxes to go with the story. On the back of the pop-up cage, draw the nightingale once it is free again.

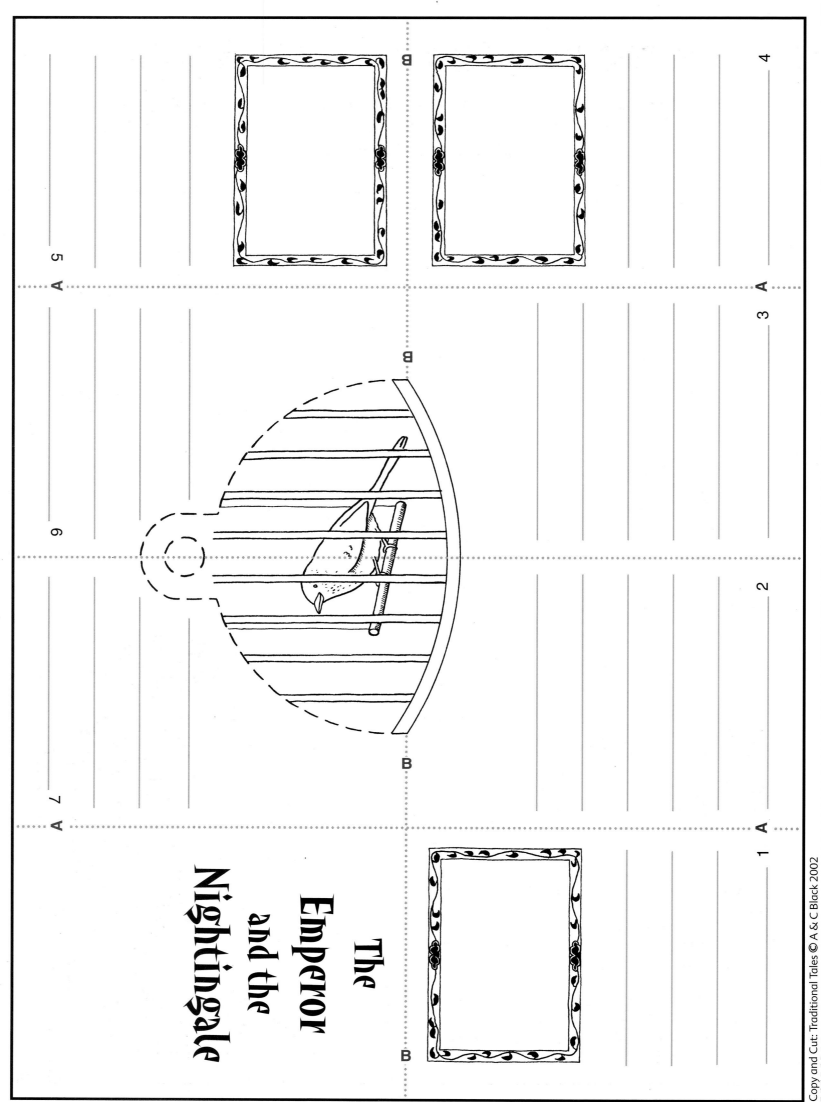

The Emperor and the Nightingale

Gingerbread Man book

Make this Gingerbread Man book to help tell the story to younger children.
You could make up your own characters or use the ones
in the traditional tale.

You will need: the Gingerbread Man book template • scissors • sticky tape • pencil •
pencil crayons for decorating

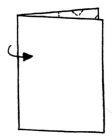 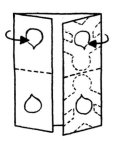 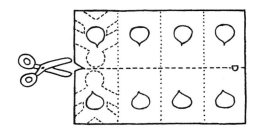

1. Fold the paper in half widthways, like this. Unfold.

2. With the blank side facing you, fold forwards along the A dots and the C dots. Unfold.

3. Cut the paper in half along the D dashes.

 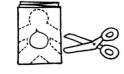

4. Fold each piece of paper in a zig-zag along the dots.

5. Cut along all the dashes to make the gingerbread man shape.

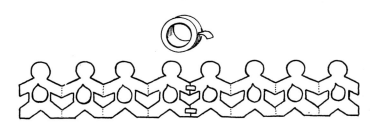

6. Now open out the shapes. Join the two strips together with sticky tape, like this.

Draw the Gingerbread Man on the first shape. Write what he says in the speech bubble.

On the second shape, draw someone who wants to eat the Gingerbread Man. Write what he or she says.

On the third shape, draw the Gingerbread Man again. On the fourth shape, draw another person. Continue like this to the end of the line.

15

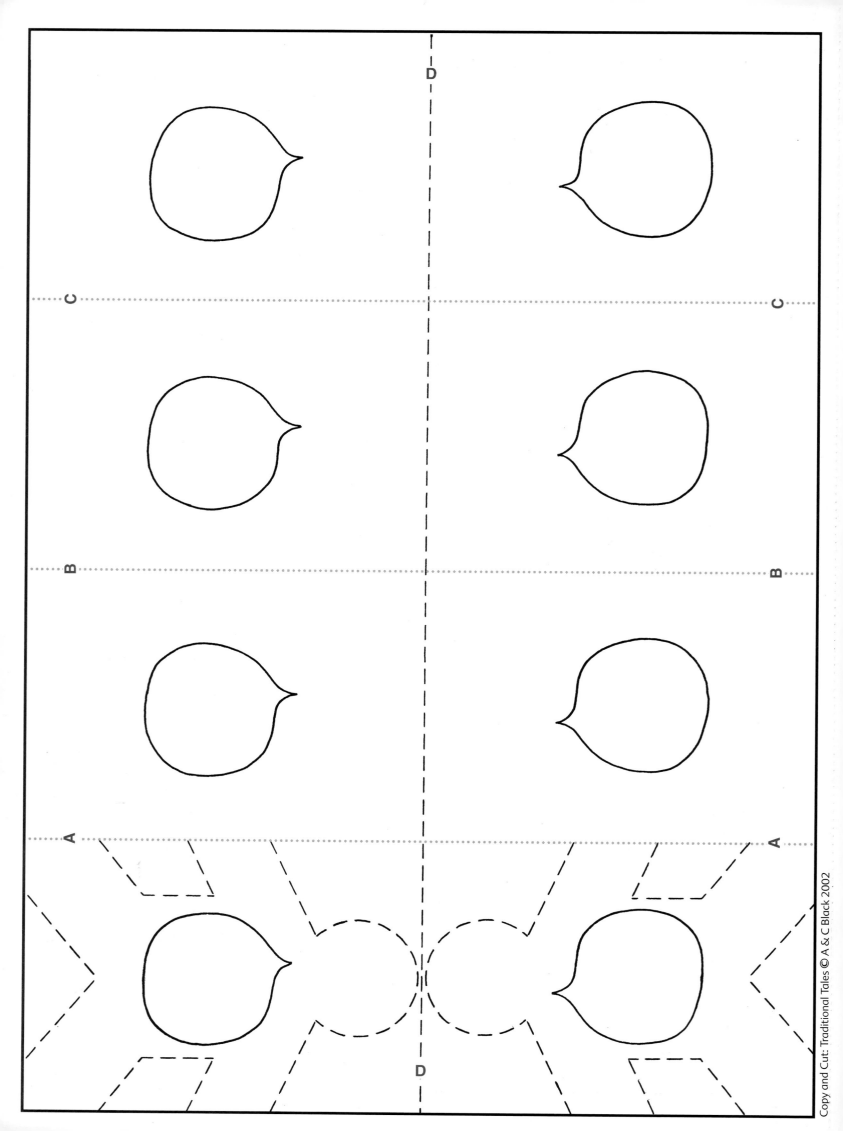

An invitation to the ball

In the story of Cinderella, there is a huge ball at the palace for Prince Charming. Imagine that you are in charge of sending out the invitations. Make this invitation to tell the guests everything they need to know.

You will need: the Invitation to the ball template • scissors • pencil • pencil crayons, gold paper, glitter and glue for decorating

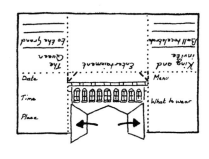

1. Cut along all the A dashes.

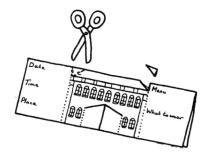

2. Fold the doors open along the dots. Unfold.

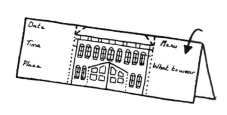

3. Fold the paper in half lengthways, like this.

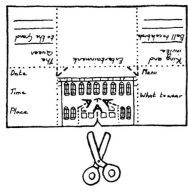

4. Fold forwards along the B dots. Unfold.

5. Cut along the C dashes.

6. Fold along the B dots again to close the invitation.

Decide who you are sending the invitation to, then fill in the gaps on the cover. Inside, write the date, time and place of the ball. Write what food there will be and what the guests should wear.

What will happen at the party? Will there be fireworks? Write this on the back. Glue on gold paper and glitter to make it look like a royal invitation.

King and

invite

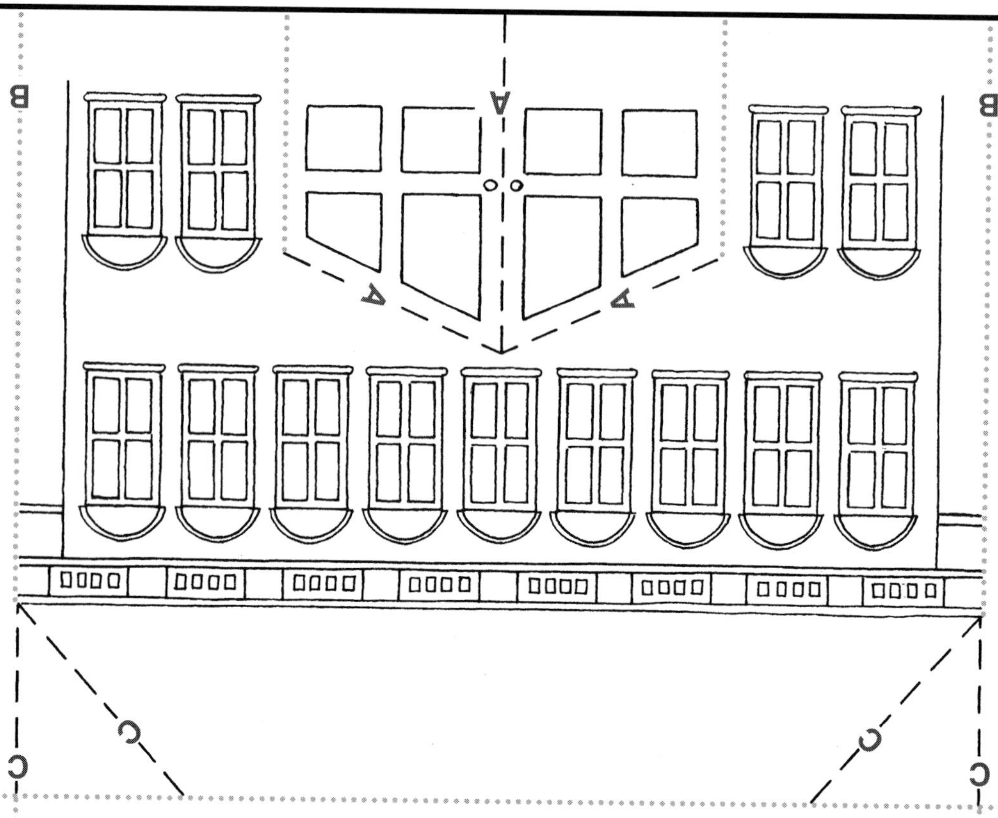

Ball to celebrate

Menu

What to wear

Entertainment

C

C

C

C

A

A

B

B

A

A

to the Grand

Queen

The

Date

Time

Place

Cinderella's diary

Imagine how Cinderella felt about all the chores she had to do. How do you think she felt when she went to the ball? Use this diary to write down Cinderella's secret thoughts and wishes.

You will need: the Cinderella's diary template • scissors • glue • pencil • pencil crayons for decorating

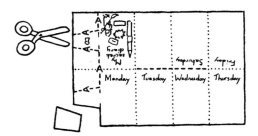

1. Cut along all the A dashes.

2. Fold the paper forwards along all the B dots. Unfold.

3. Fold the paper in half lengthways, like this. Unfold.

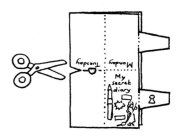

4. Fold the paper along the C dots. Cut along the D dashes. Unfold.

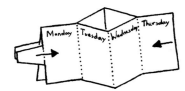

5. Fold the paper in half lengthways again. Push the left and right edges towards each other, to make a box shape in the middle.

6. Keep pushing until the sides touch. Now fold the cover around all the other pages. Fold the flaps around the book to fasten it.

Think about the details of Cinderella's daily life. Then write in the diary as though you are Cinderella. Make notes about the jobs you have to do and what the Ugly Sisters are like. Explain how you feel about the ball and what happens afterwards.

Thursday

Friday

Wednesday

Saturday

Tuesday

Monday

My
secret
diary

Do
not
open

Cinderella

Private

Magic spells book

Fairy tales are full of witches, wizards and fairy godmothers who use spells to help them perform magic. Think of spells you have read, or make up ones of your own! Write them in this handy spell book.

You will need: the Magic spells book template • scissors • glue • pencil • pencil crayons and glitter for decorating

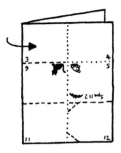 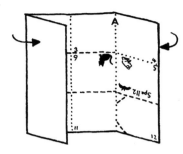 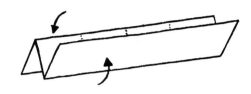

1. Fold the paper in half widthways, like this. Unfold.

2. Fold the paper forwards along all the A dots. Unfold.

3. Fold backwards along the B dots and dashes. Fold forwards along the C dots and dashes. Unfold.

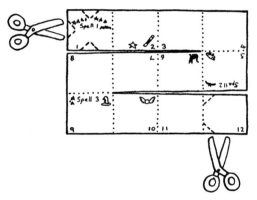 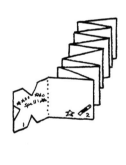 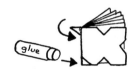

4. Cut along all the dashes.

5. Fold the paper in a zig-zag along the dots. Start by folding square 1 forwards.

6. Fold the triangles on the back cover round to the front. Glue them down.

Write a title on the cover. Inside, write your magic spells. Tell the reader when to use each spell and what it will do. Remember to list the equipment and ingredients that you will need. Explain what to do with them. Decorate the pages with glitter and bright colours.

☆ Spell 2 ☆
Use this spell when you would like a horse drawn carriage.
☆
5

You need a large pumpkin and seven mice.
Tap your wand on the wall three times.
6

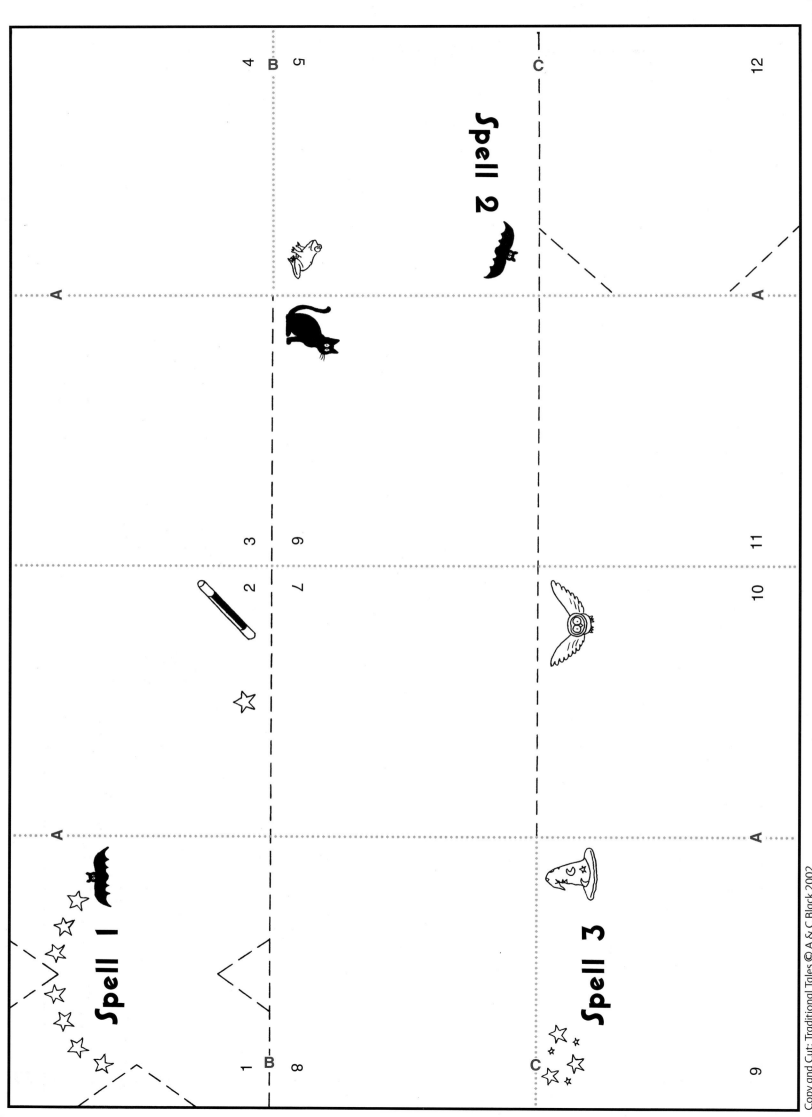

Spell 1

Spell 2

Spell 3

Seven Dwarfs book

Make up seven new dwarfs to help Snow White. Think about what your dwarfs are like and what they enjoy doing. What do they look like?
Make up names for the dwarfs.

You will need: the Seven Dwarfs book template • scissors • pencil • pencil crayons for decorating

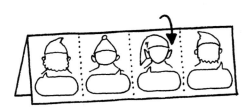

1. Fold the paper in half lengthways, like this.

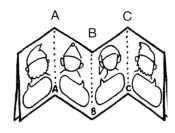

2. Fold the paper in a zig-zag along the dots (A, B, C). Start by folding forwards along the A dots.

3. Press the zig-zag flat. Cut along the dashes.

4. Open your book.

Draw a dwarf on each page. Think carefully about what each dwarf is like and what he or she does. Write the dwarf's name. Then write in the speech bubble something he or she might say.

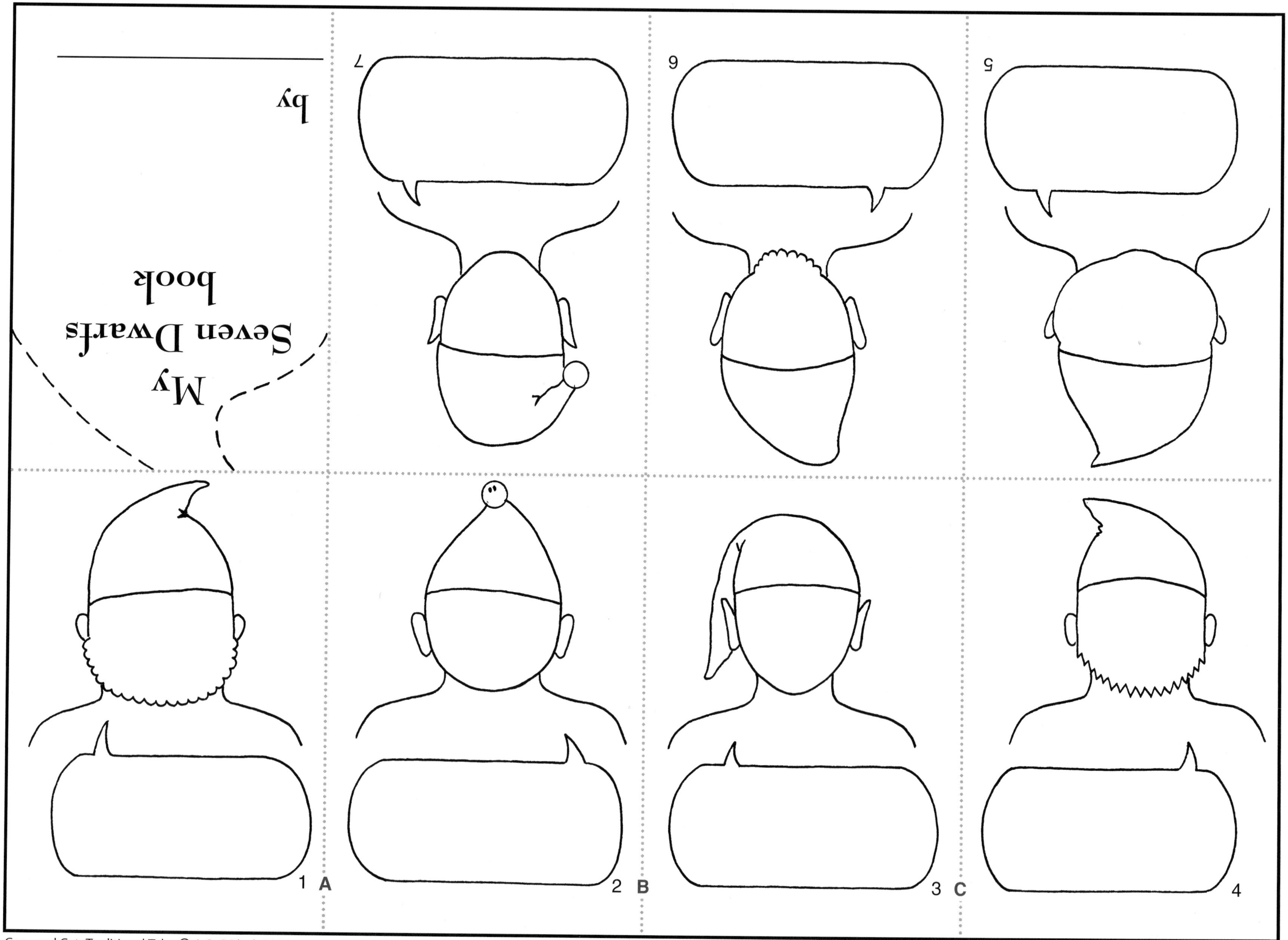

5

4

6

3 C

7

2 B

1 A

by

My
Seven Dwarfs
book

The Ugly Duckling

Baby animals change as they grow up. Some just grow bigger, but others look completely different. When the Ugly Duckling grew up, he became a beautiful swan. Use this book to re-tell the story.

You will need: the Ugly Duckling template • scissors • pencil • pencil crayons, white tissue paper and glue for decorating

1. Fold the paper in half lengthways, like this.

2. Cut along all the dashes.

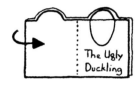

3. Fold the paper in half again, like this.

4. Fold the paper in half again, like this.

Start the story on the front cover of your book. Write inside the egg.

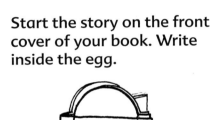

Open the cover and continue on page 1.

Then pull out the duckling picture. Write on pages 2 and 3.

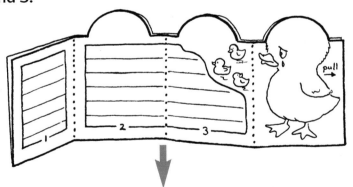

Next open out the paper fully. Finish the story on the inside. Draw a large picture of the swan. Decorate it by gluing on pieces of white tissue paper.

The Ugly Duckling

1

2

3

pull

The Frog Prince

In the story of The Frog Prince, the princess promises to let a slimy frog live with her. How do you think she really feels towards the frog? You can write the princess's secret thoughts in this special book.

You will need: the Frog Prince template • the story of The Frog Prince • scissors • glue • pencil • pencil crayons for decorating

1. Cut along all the A dashes. Put the cover and pieces E and F to one side.

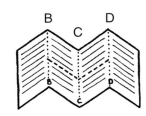

2. Fold the long strip in a zig-zag along the dots (B, C, D). Start by folding forwards along the B dots.

3. Open out the zig-zag. Then fold the paper in half. Cut along the dashes.

4. Hold the paper like this. Slot piece E into the top flap.

5. Turn the top flap. Then slot piece F into the bottom flap.

6. Fold the cover in half along the dots. Glue where marked. Place the pages inside the cover and press down.

Read the story of The Frog Prince. Then write the story in your book as though you are the princess.

Now imagine what the princess thinks to herself. Pull up the loose pages to reveal the thought bubbles. Write her secret thoughts here. Don't forget to write a title on the front cover.

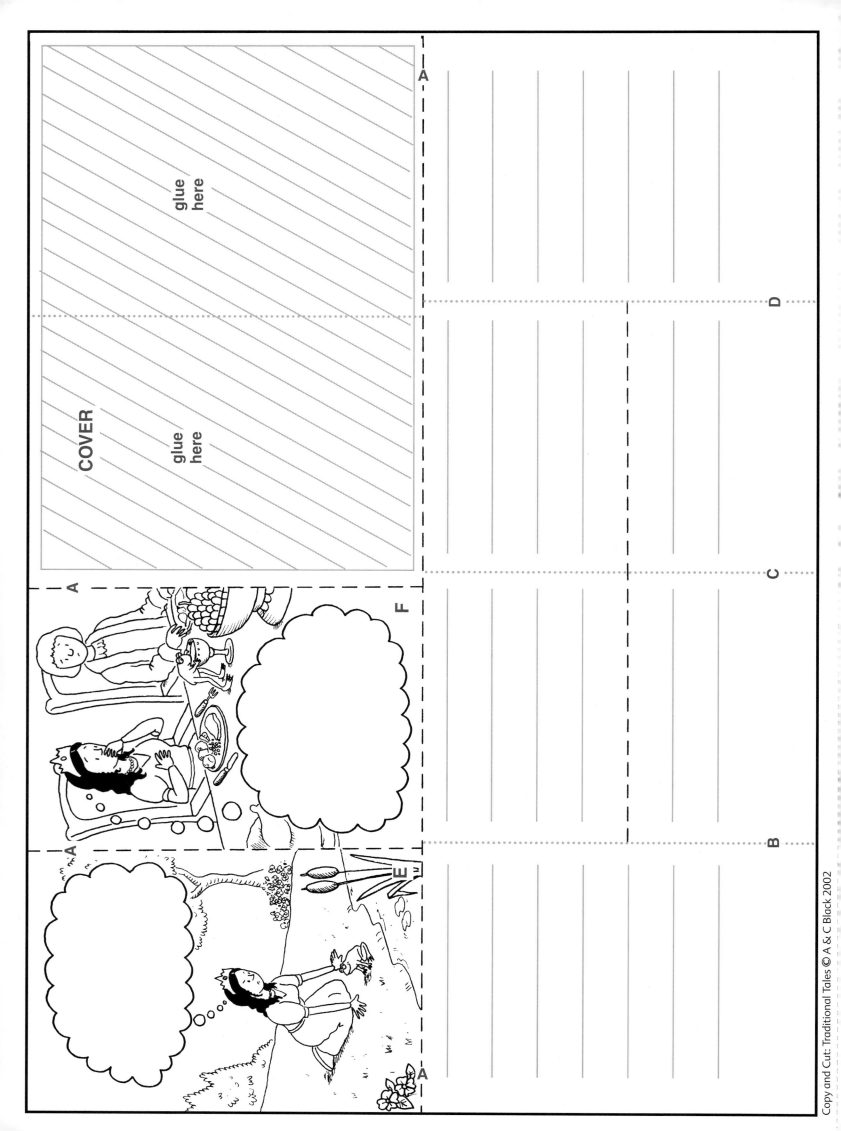

COVER

glue here

glue here

The Three Billy Goats Gruff

With a friend, make up a new version of The Three Billy Goats Gruff.
You could choose three new characters instead of the goats.
Make this model and then use it to tell your story.

You will need: the Three Billy Goats Gruff template • scissors • pencil • pencil crayons, coloured paper and glue for decorating

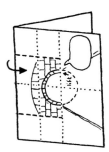

1. Fold the paper in half widthways, like this. Unfold.

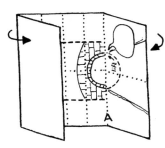

2. Fold the paper forwards along all the A dots. Unfold.

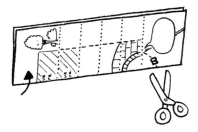

3. Fold the paper in half lengthways, like this. Cut along the B dashes. Unfold.

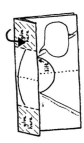

4. Fold the paper in half widthways again. Fold forwards along the C dots. Then fold backwards. Unfold.

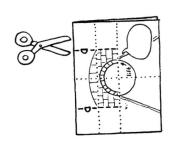

5. Cut along the D dashes. Then open out the paper.

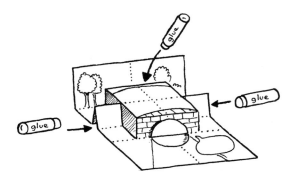

6. Lift up the bridge. Glue together the flaps at each side. Glue the back of the bridge to the back panel.

Draw and write on the model to show your new version of the story. Draw your characters. What happens when they cross the bridge? Will they try to teach the troll a lesson?

Lift the flap and draw the troll hiding under the bridge. Write what he says in the speech bubble.

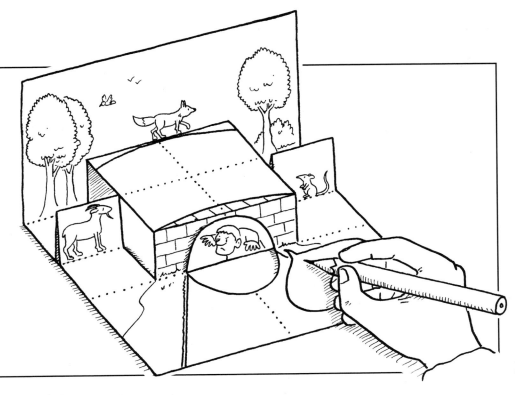

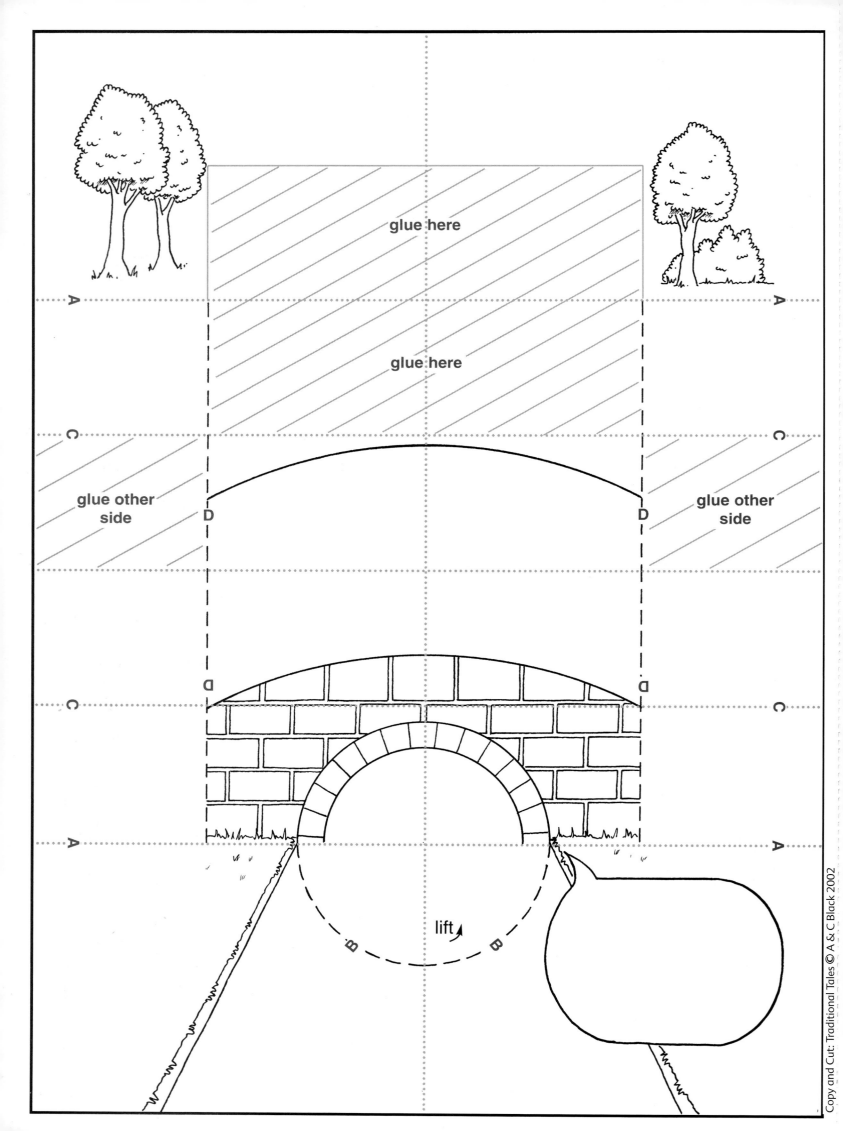

glue here

glue here

glue other side

glue other side

lift

Goldilocks and the Three Bears

You are going to make a personal organiser for Mr or Mrs Bear! A personal organiser can hold notes, lists, recipes and many other things. What do you think the bears might keep in their organiser?

You will need: the Goldilocks and the Three Bears template • eight pieces of paper measuring 7 cm x 8 cm • scissors • pencil • pencil crayons for decorating

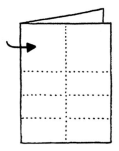

1. Fold the paper in half widthways, like this. Unfold.

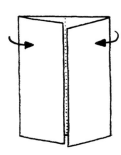

2. Fold the paper forwards along all the A dots. Unfold.

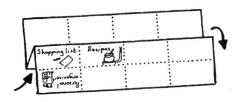

3. Fold forwards along the B dots. Fold backwards along the C dots.

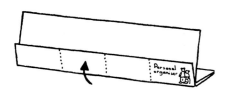

4. Turn the paper over. Fold forwards along the D dots.

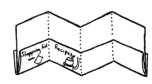

5. Turn the paper over again. Fold the paper in a zig-zag along the dots.

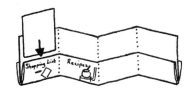

6. Slide four pieces of paper into the pockets, like this. Turn the book over and do the same on the other side.

Write a shopping list and a recipe on two of the loose pages. Then write on the rest of the pages. You could include addresses, diary notes, letters and lists of things to do. Write the name of the owner on the front cover.

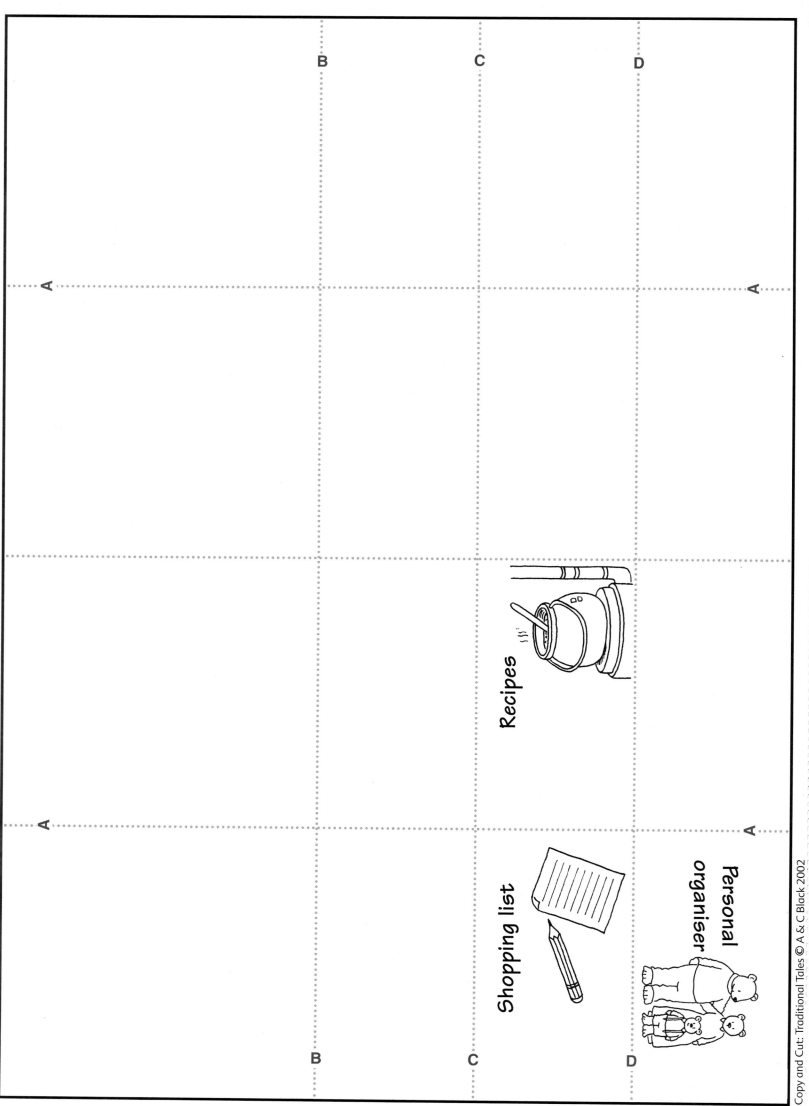

Recipes

Shopping list

Personal organiser

...And it grew bigger and bigger

In this book you can make up a story about something that grows and grows. What will you write about? Think of something really amazing that you can show growing bigger and bigger.

You will need: the ...And it grew bigger and bigger template • scissors • pencil • pencil crayons for decorating

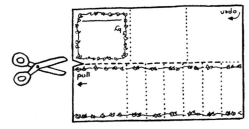

1. Cut along the dashes.

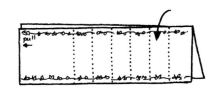

2. Fold the paper in half lengthways, like this.

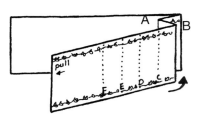

3. Fold the paper in a zig-zag along the dots (A, B, C, D, E, F). Start by folding forwards along the A dots.

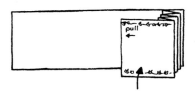

4. Press the zig-zag flat.

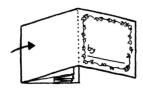

5. Fold forwards along the G dots.

6. Turn the paper over. Fold forwards along the H dots.

Write a title and the author (your name) on the front cover. Open the book and write your story.

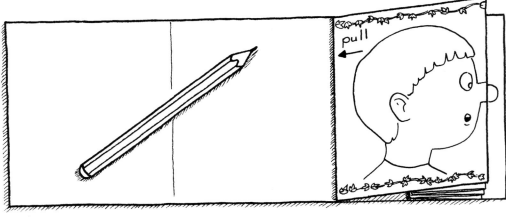

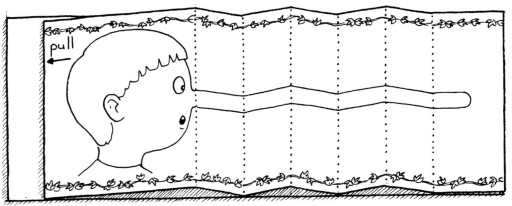

On the zig-zag, draw the thing that grows. Draw it carefully so that you can see it growing as you pull out the zig-zags one by one.

open

by
_____

pull

A

B

C

D

E

F

G

H

The Town Mouse and the Country Mouse

In the story of The Town Mouse and the Country Mouse, two mice visit each other's houses. Each mouse likes his own home best! Make this pop-up model to show the two houses.

You will need: the Town Mouse and the Country Mouse template • scissors • pencil • pencil crayons, coloured paper and glue for decorating

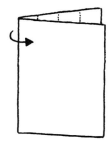

1. Fold the paper in half widthways, like this. Unfold.

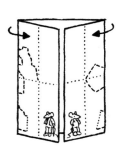

2. Turn the paper over. Fold forwards along all the A dots. Don't unfold.

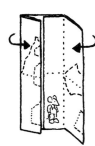

3. Fold forwards along all the B dots. Unfold along the B dots.

4. Cut along all the dashes. Fold the doors forwards along the dots. Then fold backwards. Unfold.

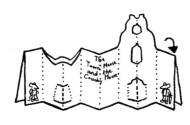

5. Open out the paper. Fold along the C dots.

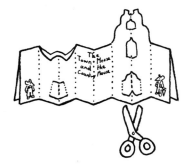

6. Cut along the dashes on the doors. Fold the doors open. Then pull the pop-up houses forwards.

Decorate the model to show a house in the country and a house in a town. You could glue on coloured paper shapes.

Discuss with a friend the advantages and disadvantages of living in the country. Then do the same for living in a town. On the back of the model, write which you would prefer.

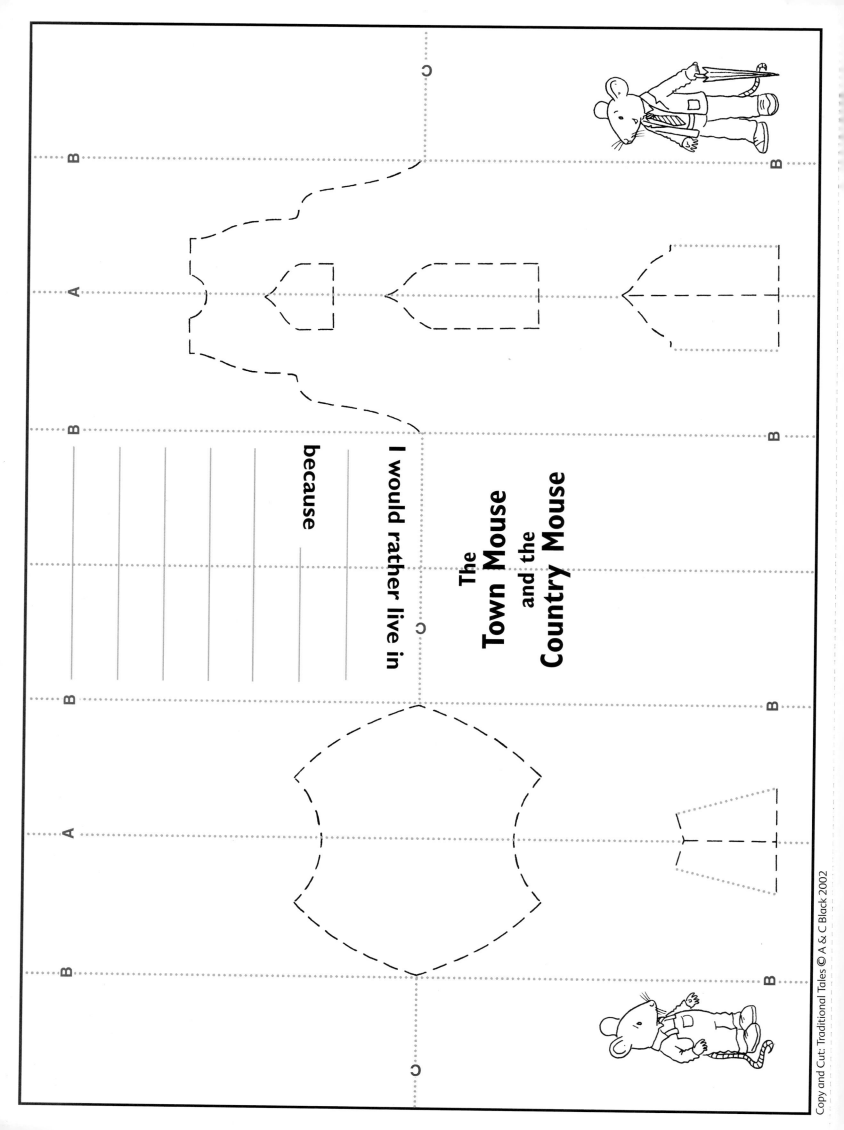

The
Town Mouse
and the
Country Mouse

I would rather live in

because

_____

_____

_____

_____

_____

_____

The Hare and the Tortoise

Be a race commentator! Use this model to show the race between the hare and the tortoise. Move the puppets along the track as you give your commentary.

You will need: the Hare and the Tortoise template • scissors • glue • pencil • pencil crayons for decorating

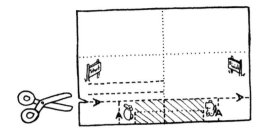

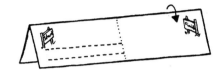

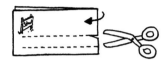

1. Cut along all the A dashes. Put the puppets to one side.

2. Fold the paper in half lengthways, like this.

3. Fold the paper in half again, like this. Cut along all the dashes.

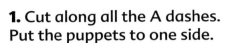

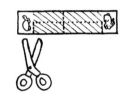

4. Unfold the paper once. Glue together the left and right edges.

5. Cut along all the dashes on the puppets.

6. Fold along the dots. Glue where marked.

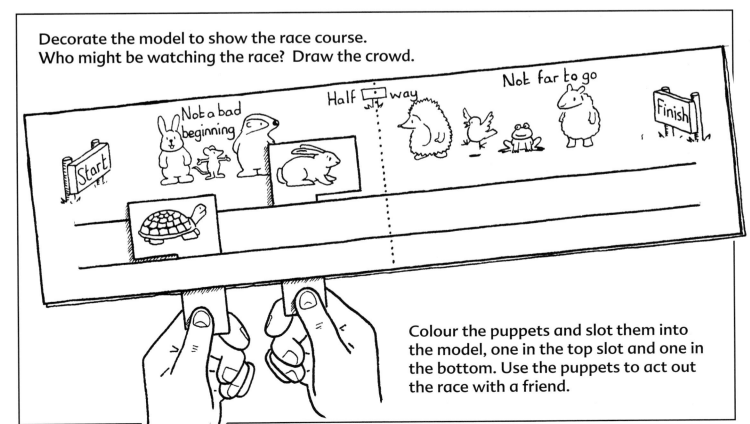

Decorate the model to show the race course.
Who might be watching the race? Draw the crowd.

Colour the puppets and slot them into the model, one in the top slot and one in the bottom. Use the puppets to act out the race with a friend.

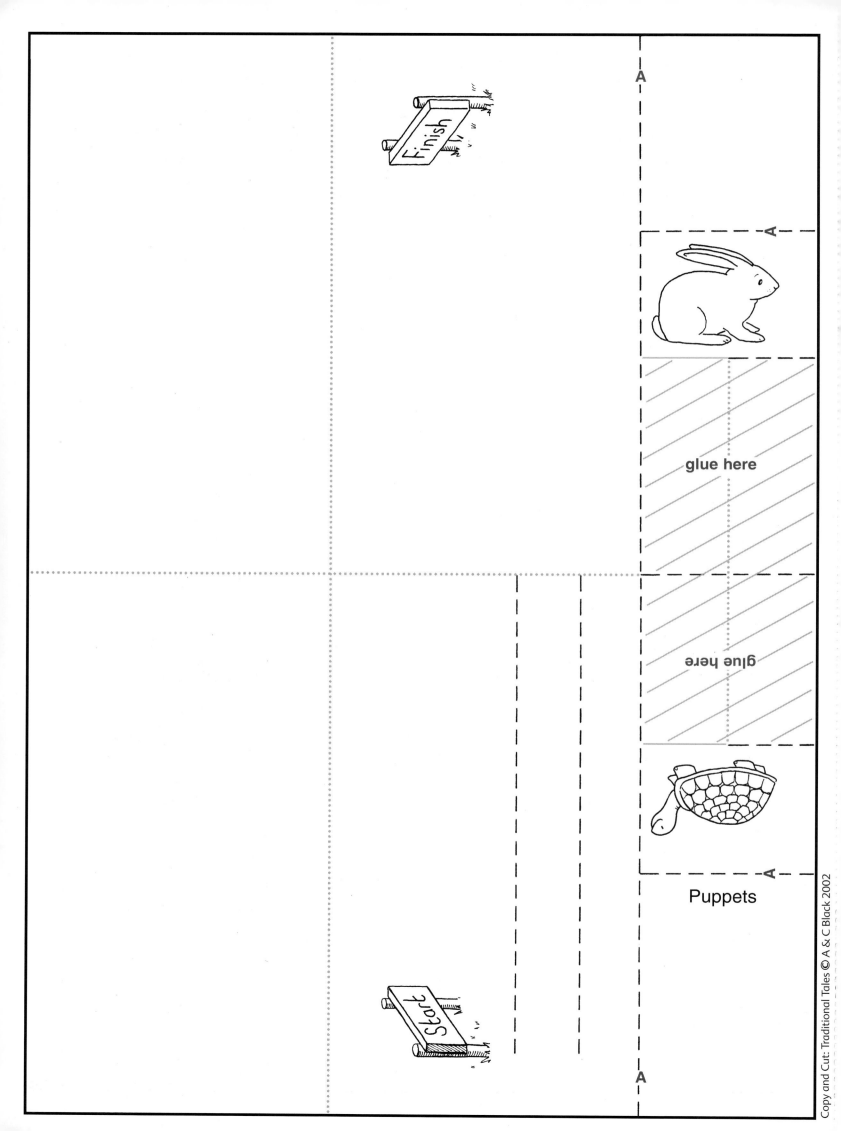

A

Finish

glue here

glue here

A

Puppets

Start

A

A

Jack and the Beanstalk

Make this beanstalk and use it to re-tell part of the story of Jack and the Beanstalk. Choose an exciting part of the story. It could be when Jack climbs the beanstalk for the first time, or when the giant chases him down.

You will need: the Jack and the Beanstalk template • scissors • glue • pencil • pencil crayons and coloured paper for decorating

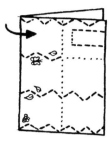

1. Fold the paper in half widthways, like this. Unfold.

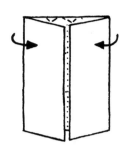

2. Fold the paper forwards along all the A dots. Unfold.

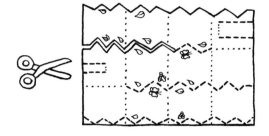

3. Cut along all the dashes.

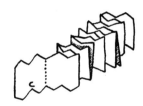

4. Fold the paper in a zig-zag along the dots. Start by folding square C forwards.

5. On square D, fold the flap along the B dots. Then glue the rest of the square to the paper beneath.

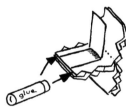

6. Do the same on square E.

Write your story on the beanstalk. Make the description as lively as you can. Remember to include what the characters say and think. Draw characters or animals on the flaps, or draw them on coloured paper and glue them on.

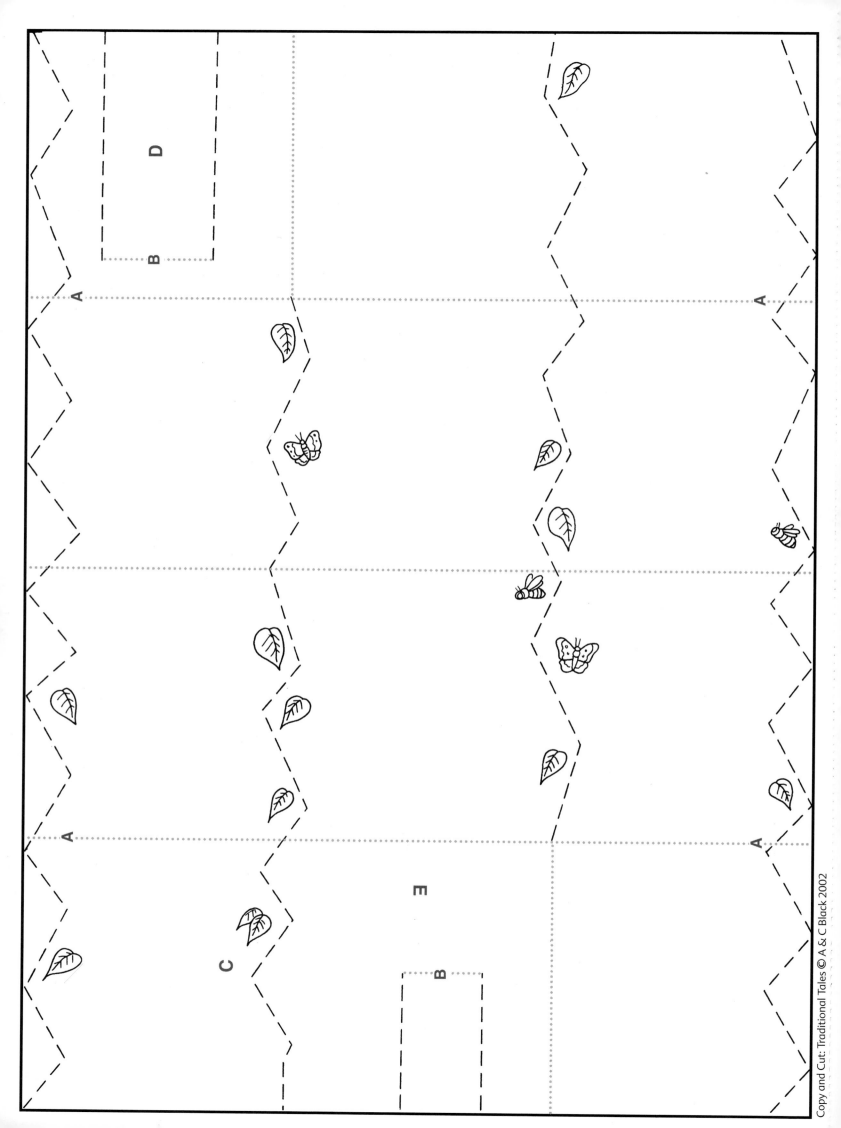

Hansel and Gretel house

In the story of Hansel and Gretel, the witch's house is made of mouth-watering sweets and cakes. The wicked witch wants to tempt children inside. Make your own magical house and decorate it with colourful sweets.

You will need: the Hansel and Gretel house template • scissors • glue • pencil • pencil crayons, coloured paper or card and sweet wrappers for decorating

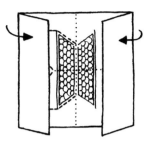

1. Fold the paper forwards along all the A dots. Unfold.

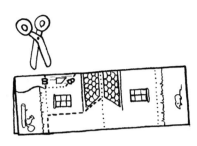

2. Fold the paper in half lengthways. Cut along the B dashes. Unfold.

3. Fold the paper in half widthways. Cut along the dashes to make the house shape. Unfold.

4. Cut along the dashes on the door. Fold the doors open along the dots.

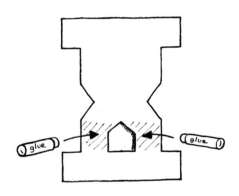

5. Turn the paper over. Spread glue only at each side of the door.

6. Fold the paper in half again and press together. Push the base flat to make the house stand up.

Make sweets from coloured paper or card. You could also use sweet wrappers. Make them look as realistic and delicious as you can. Glue them on to the front and back of the house so that the whole house seems to be made of sweets. You could draw the witch inside the doorway.

The Sleeping Beauty

Think about what happens in the story of The Sleeping Beauty. What are the characters like? Tell the story on this castle, or make up your own fairy tale about 'good' and 'evil' characters.

You will need: the Sleeping Beauty template • scissors • pencil • pencil crayons for decorating

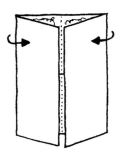

1. Fold the paper forwards along all the A dots. Unfold.

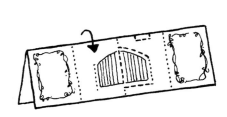

2. Fold the paper in half lengthways, like this. Unfold.

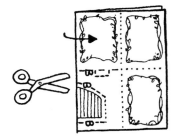

3. Fold the paper in half widthways. Cut along the B dashes. Unfold.

4. Fold the paper in half lengthways. Then fold the paper in half again, like this. Cut along the C dashes.

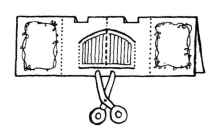

5. Unfold the paper once. Cut along the dashes on the door. Fold the doors open along the dots.

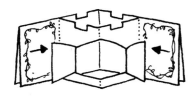

6. Push the left and right edges towards each other to make the model stand up.

Press the model flat and write your story at the sides of the castle doors. Continue on the back of the model. Don't forget to give it a title! Open the doors and draw a scene inside. Colour the outside of the castle.

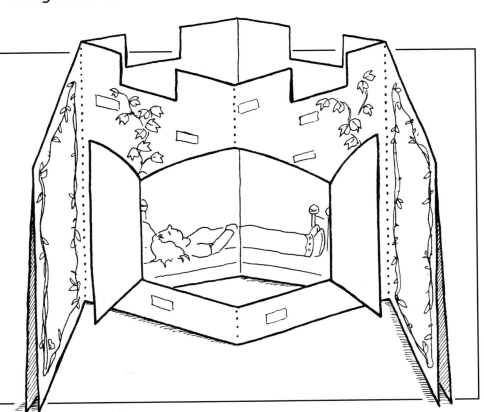

43

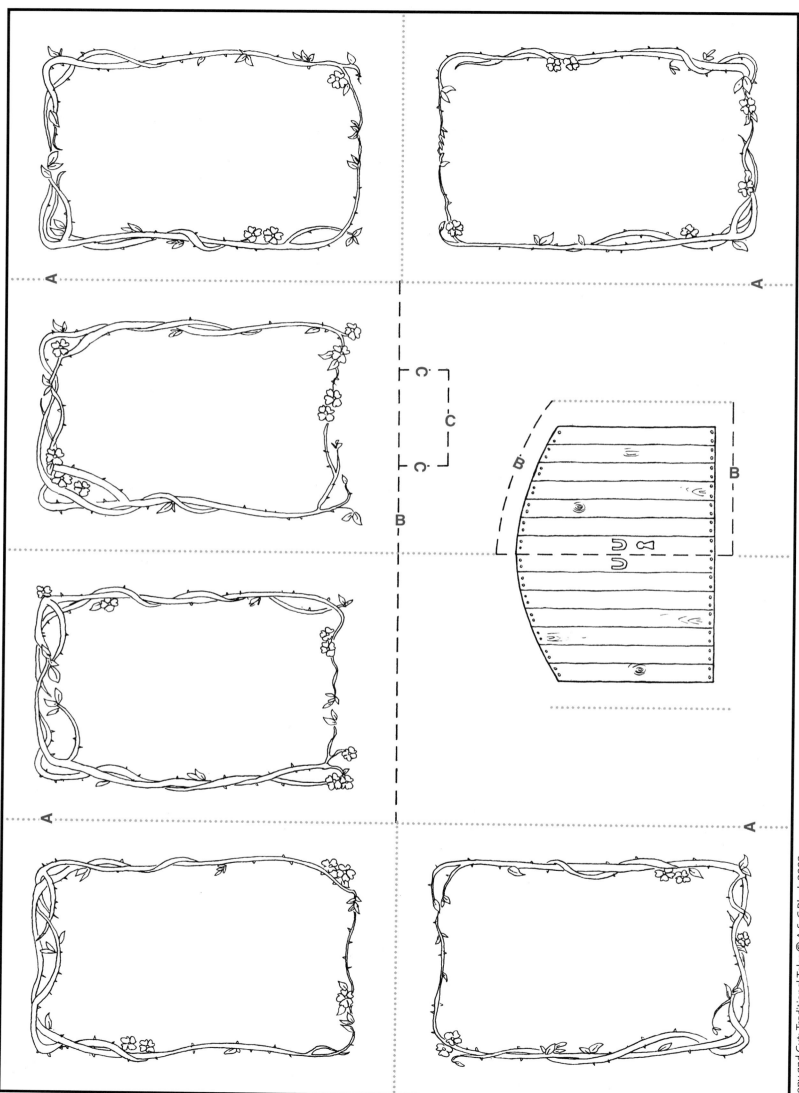

Pig mask

With three friends, you can act out the story of The Three Little Pigs. Decide together who will be the pigs and who will be the wolf. Make this pig mask to wear when you act out the story.

You will need: the Pig mask template • scissors • glue • a length of elastic • pencil • pencil crayons and coloured paper for decorating

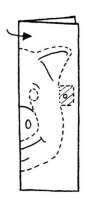

1. Fold the paper in half lengthways, like this.

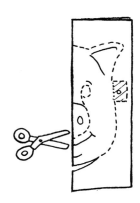

2. Cut along all the dashes. Unfold.

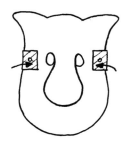

3. Turn the paper over. Fold the tabs along the dots. Then unfold.

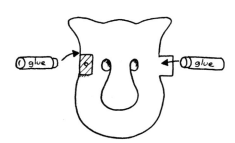

4. Spread glue on the back of the tabs and glue them to the mask.

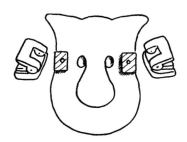

5. Use a hole puncher to make holes in the circles.

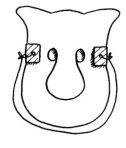

6. Cut a length of elastic to fit your head. Tie it through the holes.

Colour the mask and decorate it by gluing on coloured paper. Make notes about what your pig does and what he says. Put on your mask and act out the story of The Three Little Pigs with your friends.

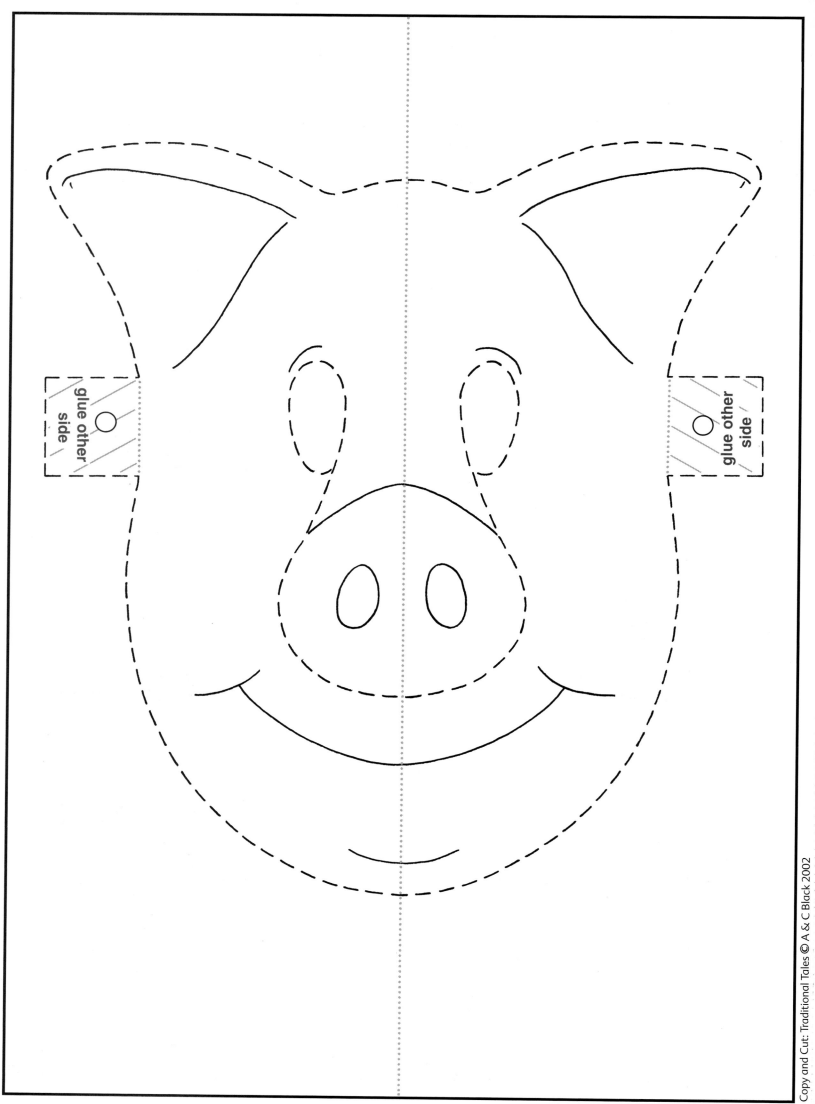

glue other side

glue other side

Wolf mask

With three friends, you can act out the story of The Three Little Pigs. Decide together who will be the pigs and who will be the wolf. Make this wolf mask to wear when you act out the story.

You will need: the Wolf mask template • scissors • glue • a length of elastic • pencil • pencil crayons and grey paper or felt for decorating

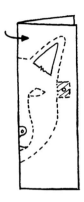

1. Fold the paper in half lengthways, like this.

2. Cut along all the dashes. Unfold.

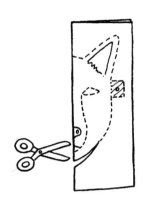

3. Turn the paper over. Fold the tabs along the dots. Then unfold.

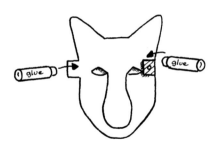

4. Spread glue on the back of the tabs and glue them to the mask.

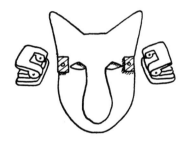

5. Use a hole puncher to make holes in the circles.

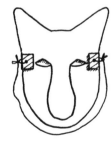

6. Cut a length of elastic to fit your head. Tie it through the holes.

Colour the mask and glue on grey paper or felt. Make the wolf look as fierce as you can. Make notes about what the wolf does and what he says. Put on your mask and act out the story of The Three Little Pigs with your friends.

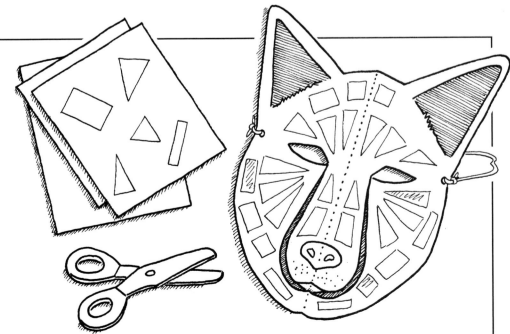
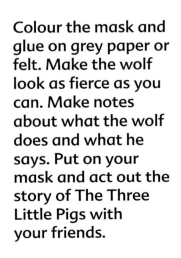

glue other side

glue other side

The Little Red Hen

You are going to make a storybook of The Little Red Hen for younger children. Read the story and notice what the animals say. For your story, you could choose different animals instead of the cat, rat and pig.

You will need: the Little Red Hen template • the story of The Little Red Hen • scissors • pencil • pencil crayons for decorating

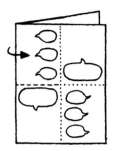 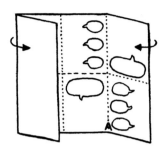 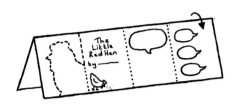

1. Fold the paper in half widthways, like this. Unfold.

2. Fold the paper forwards along all the A dots. Unfold.

3. Fold the paper in half lengthways, like this. Unfold.

 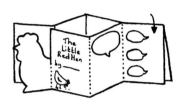 

4. Cut along all the dashes.

5. Fold the paper lengthways again.

6. Fold the zig-zags into a book, with the hen on the front cover.

Draw an animal next to each speech bubble and write in the speech bubbles. Continue the story on the other side of the book (you will need to draw your own speech bubbles). Don't forget to illustrate the front cover!

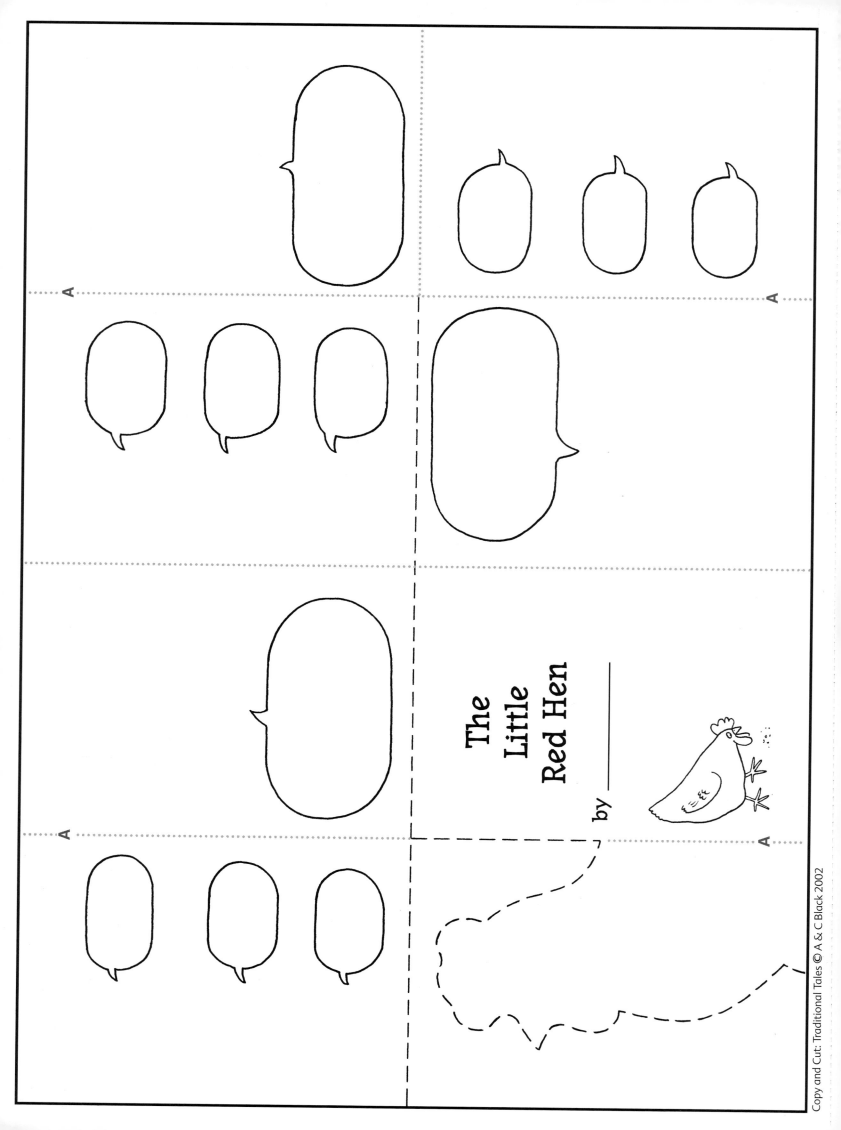

The
Little
Red Hen

by _____

Little Red Riding Hood Map

Use this story map to help you re-tell the story of Little Red Riding Hood. Think about the places in the story, such as Grandma's house. What else can you draw on the map to help you tell the story?

You will need: the Little Red Riding Hood map template • scissors • pencil • pencil crayons for decorating

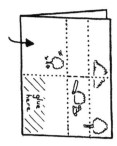

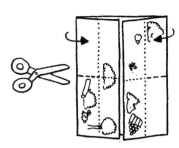

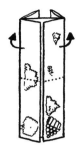

1. Fold the paper in half widthways, like this. Unfold.

2. With the blank side facing you, fold forwards along all the A dots. Cut along all the dashes.

3. Fold backwards along all the B dots. Then open out the paper.

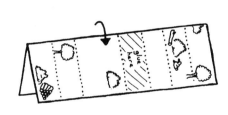

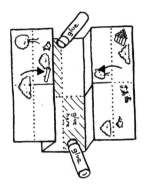

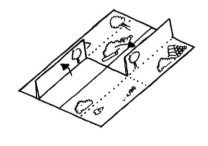

4. Fold the paper in half lengthways, like this. Unfold.

5. Spread glue where marked. Fold the edges in and press flat.

6. Lift up the flaps.

Draw the cottages on the pop-up flaps. Draw the path through the woods. Add extra details to make the setting look realistic. You could draw characters on a separate piece of paper and cut them out. Move them around the map as you tell the story.

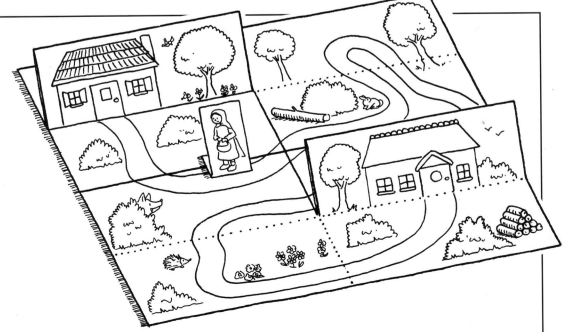

B

B

glue here

glue here

A

A

A

A

B

B

Letter to a story character

Choose a character from a story you know well. What would you like to say to the character? What questions would you like to ask? Make this special folding letter and write to your character.

You will need: the Letter to a story character template • scissors • pencil • pencil crayons for decorating

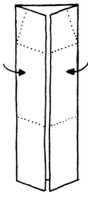

1. Start with the blank side facing you. Fold forwards along all the A dots.

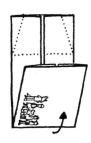

2. Fold forwards along the B dots.

3. Fold forwards along all the C dots.

4. Fold forwards along the D dots.

5. Tuck the flap inside the letter.

Open out the paper again. Write your letter on the inside. Think about the best way to begin and end the letter. When you have finished writing, fold up the letter again. Write the name and address on the front.

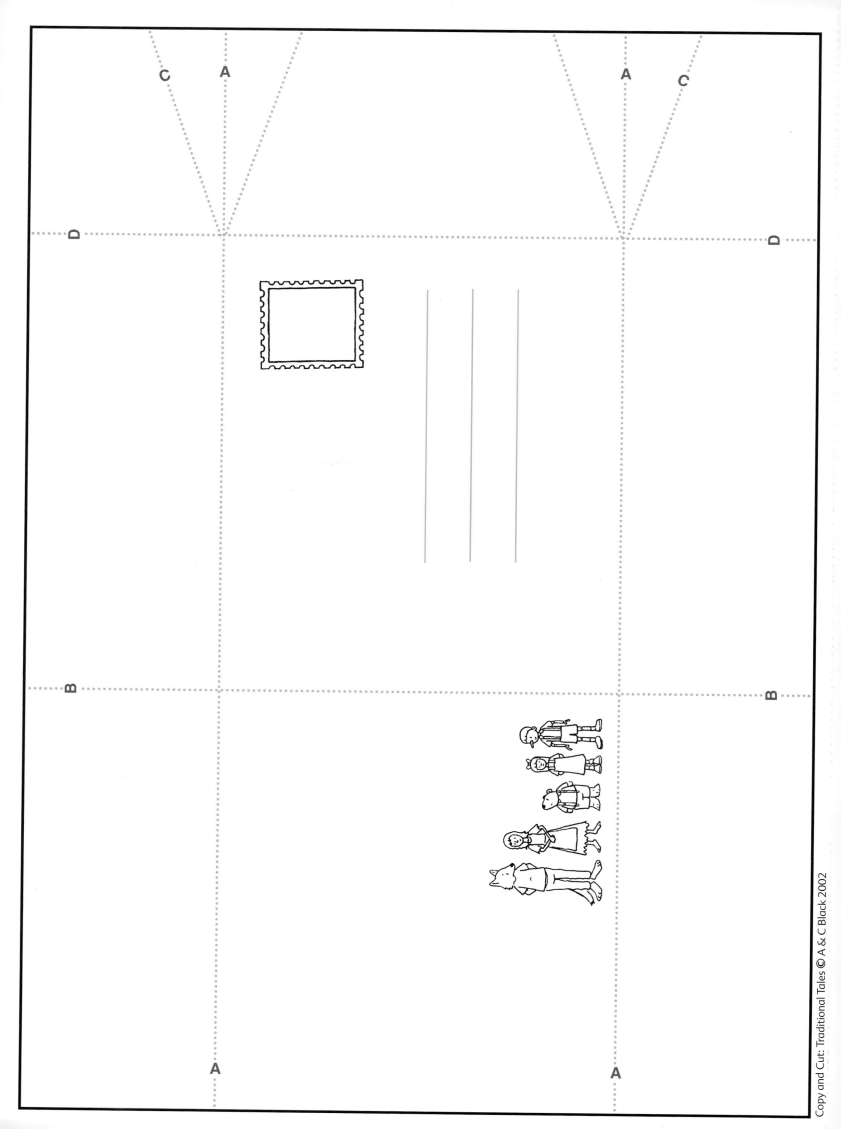

Anansi and the Banana Bird

The place to find the Banana Bird was, of course, on the branches of a banana tree — if you could make out his banana-yellow-and-black feathers. There was another animal in the forest who liked bananas too. That was Anansi the spider.

Anansi's big eyes spotted the Banana Bird. "I nearly ate you by mistake," he said. "You look just like a banana!"

"I might look like a banana, but I can move a lot faster than you can, with my big yellow-and-black-feathered wings. I'll race you to the place where the brightest, yellowest, tastiest bananas grow. The winner can have all the best bananas there."

Anansi agreed. The Banana Bird laughed at the idea of a spider moving as quickly as a bird with big banana-yellow-and-black wings. And so off they went.

The Banana Bird knew he had plenty of time. He stopped to feast on mangoes and coconuts. Then he asked other animals where the best bananas were. At last, he flew to the top of the tree which had the brightest, yellowest, tastiest bananas.

There was Anansi, munching happily.

The Banana Bird couldn't believe his eyes. "How did you get here so quickly?" he squawked.

"Well," said Anansi, "While you were busy talking and eating mangoes and coconuts, I spun a huge web from branch to branch. I kept spinning and climbing until I found the tree which has the brightest, yellowest, tastiest bananas."

The Banana Bird's banana-yellow-and-black feathers quivered with anger. His big banana-yellow-and-black beak wobbled. He flapped his wings and flew away until he was a little black dot in the sky.

Anansi smiled and carried on munching.

The Blue Jackal

The jackal was hungry, but it was hard work hunting and killing other animals for food. It was easier to creep into the city and steal scraps from the rubbish. So that was what he did. He slunk off alone, leaving the rest of the pack behind in the forest.

Suddenly the jackal sniffed. A delicious smell was drifting from somewhere. He sniffed along an alley, through a doorway and down some steps. Then his paw slipped on something wet, and he fell with a splash into a big tub of water! He paddled and swam, splashed and scrambled, and pulled himself out. He raced back to the forest.

The other animals did not recognise the jackal. He was blue! He had fallen into a tub of dye, not water. When the jackal realised this, he had an idea.

"I am Fierce Claw," he said. "Indra, the king of the gods, sent me down to Earth to rule the forest."

The other animals bowed down before Fierce Claw. He gave important jobs to the lion, the elephant and the tiger. The jackals offered to help, but Fierce Claw drove them away. He knew they would soon guess who he was.

The animals hunted for food and brought it to Fierce Claw. He no longer had to hunt if he felt hungry. He lived like a king.

One day Fierce Claw heard the other jackals howling at the edge of the forest. Before he could stop himself, he joined in with a mighty howl. Straight away the forest fell silent. Then the angry, snarling pack of jackals chased Fierce Claw out of the forest. He was never allowed to return.

Copy and Cut: Traditional Tales © A & C Black 2002

Two Heads are Better than One

Elephant was big and strong but not very clever; Monkey was clever but not very big or strong. Which was better, they wondered, strength or cleverness? They went to ask Owl. She was the wisest animal in the kingdom.

Owl thought for a moment, then pointed to a tall fruit tree across the river. She told them to collect some fruit from the tree.

At first Monkey was afraid because he could not swim. So Elephant swam across the river with Monkey riding on his back.

When they reached the tree, Elephant realised that his trunk was not long enough to reach the fruit. But Monkey knew what to do. He quickly climbed the tree and returned clutching the fruit in his paw.

They went back to Owl with the fruit.

"Neither of you could have reached the fruit alone," said Owl. "But your strength, Elephant, and your brains, Monkey, meant that you could collect the fruit together."

The Little Red Hen

One day the Little Red Hen found some grains of wheat in the farmyard.

"Who will help me to plant the grain?" she asked the other animals. "Not I," said the pig. "Not I," said the cat. "Not I," said the rat. So she did it herself.

The grains grew shoots. "Who will help me to water and weed?" she asked. "Not I," said the pig. "Not I," said the cat. "Not I," said the rat. So she did it herself.

Soon the wheat ripened. "Who will help me to harvest and mill?" she asked. "Not I," said the pig. "Not I," said the cat. "Not I," said the rat. So she did it herself.

The wheat was turned into flour. "Who will help me to bake a loaf?" she asked. "Not I," said the pig. "Not I," said the cat. "Not I," said the rat. So she did it herself.

"Who will help me to eat the bread?" she asked. "I will," said the pig. "I will," said the cat. "I will," said the rat. But the Little Red Hen ate it all herself!

The Emperor and the Nightingale

The emperor of China had a beautiful garden where a nightingale lived. The nightingale sang so sweetly that everyone passing by would stop and listen. Poets wrote poems about it. Soon crowds of people gathered to hear the bird sing.

One day the emperor said to his courtiers, "Why are all those people standing outside the palace garden?"

They told him about the nightingale. "Bring it to me," said the emperor. A maid caught the little brown bird and brought it into the palace.

The nightingale's song was the most wonderful music the emperor had ever heard. "Keep it here, so that I can listen to it every evening," he said. The nightingale sang for the emperor, but its song became sad because it wanted to fly in the garden.

Then someone sent the emperor a present. It was a singing clockwork bird. Its feathers sparkled with jewels, unlike the dull brown feathers of the real bird. The emperor and courtiers were enchanted with it. No one noticed when the real nightingale broke free and escaped into the garden.

Before long the clockwork bird began to rattle, and finally it stopped working. Soon afterwards the emperor fell ill. He was close to death, when the nightingale came to sing at his window. As soon as the emperor heard the music, he recovered.

"Please come back into my palace," he said to the nightingale.

"I will not," replied the bird, "but I promise to sing at your window every night." The nightingale kept its promise and the emperor lived a long and happy life.

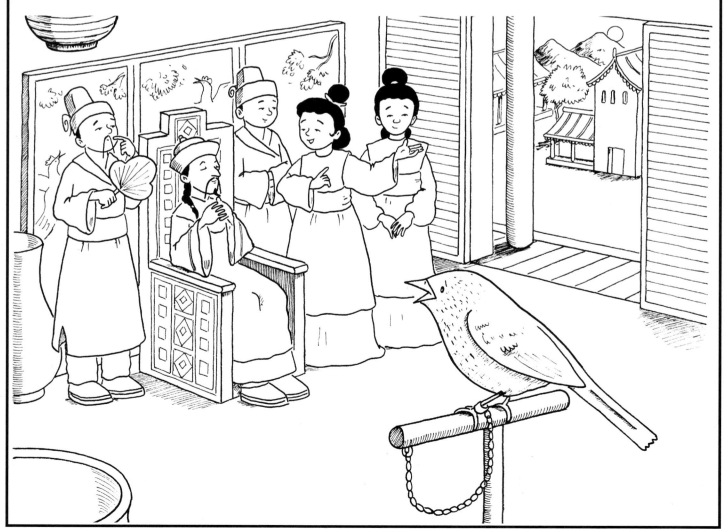

Copy and Cut: Traditional Tales © A & C Black 2002

The Frog Prince

The youngest princess loved to play with her ball. But it was no ordinary ball — it was made of pure gold. One day the ball fell with a splash into the pond in the palace garden. The princess sobbed as if her heart would break.

Suddenly, a frog hopped out on to the grass beside the princess. He croaked, "I can fetch your ball for you."

"Oh, please do, and I shall give you anything you want," cried the princess.

"Anything?" asked the frog.

"Anything," said the princess.

"I shall help you if you promise to marry me," said the frog. The princess laughed, but the frog carried on. "Promise to let me eat from your golden plate, drink from your golden cup and sleep in your beautiful bed. Then I shall fetch the ball."

"Very well, I promise," she said. So the frog dived into the pond and found the ball. The princess clapped her hands in glee and ran off with it to the palace. The frog hopped slowly after her.

At supper the princess tried to make the frog go away. But the king asked her what the frog wanted. When the princess told him, the king said, "You have made a promise. Now you must let the frog eat from your golden plate and drink from your golden cup."

At bedtime, the princess set off alone up the big staircase. At once the frog followed, croaking, "Carry me with you." The princess shivered with disgust at the thought of picking him up. Then the king said, "This is no way to treat someone who helped you. Take him with you."

The princess put the frog in the corner of her room, but as soon as she got into bed he hopped up beside her. "Give me a kiss," he said. The princess closed her eyes in horror and put out her lips. To her surprise she felt warm skin instead of a cold slimy froggy face. She opened her eyes and there was a handsome prince.

The prince told her how a magic spell had turned him into a frog. The only thing that could break the spell was a kiss from a princess.

Helpful hints

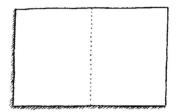 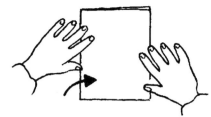 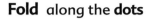

Fold along the **dots**

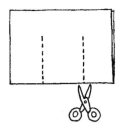

Cut along the **dashes**

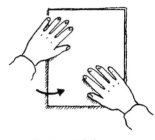 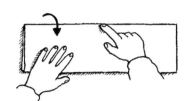

fold **widthways**   fold **lengthways**

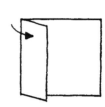 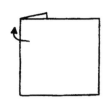

fold **forwards**   fold **backwards**

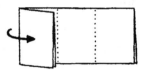 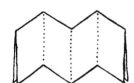

Zig-zag
Fold forwards along the first dotted line.
Fold backwards along the second dotted line.
Fold forwards along the third dotted line.
Continue until you reach the end.

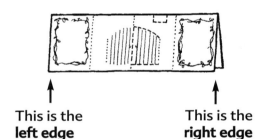

This is the **left edge**   This is the **right edge**

Using glue

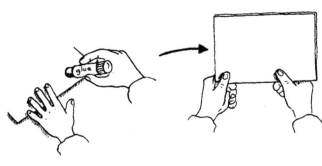 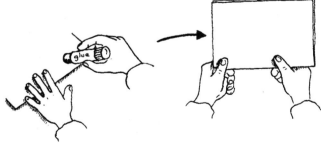

Use very small amounts of glue. Press together
the pieces you have glued to help them stick.

Using scissors

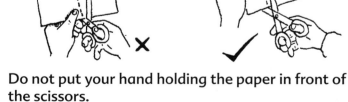

Do not put your hand holding the paper in front of
the scissors.

Close the scissors when you are not using them.

Make sure the scissors don't get hidden under
pieces of paper.

Teachers' notes

by Christine Moorcroft

Anansi character tree (pages 5–6)

Give the children copies of the story of Anansi and the Banana Bird (page 55) for them to read and plan their character descriptions. Tell them that this story is a traditional tale from the Caribbean, then show them photographs of the Caribbean and locate it on a map of the world. After reading the story with the children, ask them what Anansi is like, and how they can tell (supporting their answers with examples from the story). Then do the same for the Banana Bird. Explain that they are going to write a very short character description. Point out the small amount of writing space on the tree; the children should make notes, edit them, and write the final version on the tree. Some children will need help with fitting the pieces together.

The Blue Jackal (pages 7–8)

Give the children copies of the story of The Blue Jackal (page 56) for them to read and plan what they want to write in their books. Before reading it, ask them what kind of animal a jackal is; show them pictures of jackals and explain that they are common in African countries, southern Europe and India but not in Britain. Read and discuss the story with the class; draw out that the blue jackal was greedy and lazy. Ask the children why he drove the other jackals out of the forest, and why he joined in with the howling of the pack when he would have been safe if he had kept quiet (he could not resist doing what jackals do naturally). Invite the children to explain why the pack of jackals banished the blue jackal and to identify the moral of the story.

Two Heads are Better than One (pages 9–10)

Give the children copies of the story of Two Heads are Better than One (page 57) for them to read and plan what they want to write in their books. Before reading it, ask them which they think is more important — to be strong or to be clever. They should support their answers with examples. Read the story together and discuss the moral: that each quality is important in a different way, and that two people can achieve more working together than they can alone. Discuss other situations in which two animals or people could combine strength and cleverness (or two other qualities, such as skill in music and skill in reading, or skill with numbers and speed in running). The children could plan and write another story around one of the situations they think of.

Three wishes book (pages 11–12)

Talk about the story of Aladdin and what happened when he polished the lamp. Ask the children if they have been to any special places where they have made wishes. Invite them to share their wishes and to decide what they would wish for if they had a magic lamp. They could begin by writing all the wishes they can think of and then choosing the three things they want most of all. Talk about the language of wishes (I wish, I would like, so that, if, to). Point out the forms of the verbs: there will be a combination of present tense and conditional.

The Emperor and the Nightingale (pages 13–14)

Give the children copies of the story of The Emperor and the Nightingale (page 58) for them to read and plan what they want to write in their books. This story was originally written by Hans Christian Andersen. Prepare for the lesson by collecting enough small pictures of nightingales for each group to see, or one large poster-sized picture. If possible, find a sound or video recording of a nightingale singing (available to buy from *www.birdfood.co.uk/shop/*). In a calm, quiet atmosphere, play the sound or video recording and encourage the children to talk about their responses to the sound of the bird. Discuss why people might want to keep a nightingale and listen to it whenever they want to. Tell them that they are going to read a story from China in which an emperor did just that.

Gingerbread Man book (pages 15–16)

Explain to the children that they are going to make a book for younger children, telling part of the story of *The Gingerbread Man*. Ask them about the story and if they know what the Gingerbread Man says. Emphasise that he uses exactly the same words each time he speaks: 'Run, run, as fast as you can. You can't catch me I'm the Gingerbread Man!' The children should choose part of this text to write on their books. (To give more writing space, enlarge the template to A3 size.) Discuss the repeated words of the people who want to eat the Gingerbread Man: 'Come here! Let me eat you.' Ask the children to use repeated phrases in the speech bubbles, alternating the Gingerbread Man with other people.

An invitation to the ball (pages 17–18)

Before the lesson, collect invitations to a variety of events. Give each group several invitations to examine, and ask them to list the important information: the names of the sender and recipient, title and description of the event, date, start and finish time, venue, details for replying (to whom, at what address, by what date) and, possibly, dress code. Discuss useful vocabulary and the types of language that could be used. Give copies of the story of Cinderella to the children (use the Grimm or Perrault original, available in Penguin Classics, or an abridged version). Ask them to read it and to record relevant information on a chart. They could address their invitation to the Ugly Sisters. They can make up other details, based on what they can gather from the story.

From	To
Event	Place
Date	Start time
Finish time	Reply to (name and address)

Cinderella's diary (pages 19—20)

The children should first have read some published diaries, or books written in diary form. You could make up the diary of a fictional character, writing entries in note form on diary pages, and photocopy it for the children to read (perhaps on an overhead transparency). Discuss the type of language (formal or informal, personal or impersonal) and how we can tell: from the person, vocabulary and the pronouns used to refer to the reader and the writer. A diary might be written in note form, and it might be difficult for other people to follow because they may not know about the people and things referred to; remind the children that a diary is usually written only for the writer and not for any other audience. Ask the children to make notes from the story of *Cinderella* about the kinds of things Cinderella did each day (the chores and the unkind words and actions of the Ugly Sisters), and about the fairy godmother's visit and the ball. Point out that the diary has six days so they will need to plan what parts of the story to include. Remind them to use the first person and to think about the kind of language used in a diary.

Magic spells book (pages 21—22)

Ask the children about books or poems they have read which contain magic spells, for example, *Snow White and the Seven Dwarfs*, *The Sleeping Beauty*, *Baba Yaga*, *Harry Potter and the Philosopher's Stone* (or other Harry Potter books), the witches' spell from Shakespeare's *Macbeth*, *The Sorcerer's Apprentice*. Talk about the purposes of spells in stories. Also show the children instruction leaflets and recipe books, and talk about the way in which the instructions or recipes are set out: there is a description or picture of what will be achieved, a list of equipment and/or ingredients, and step by step instructions. Discuss the language of instructions: short sentences, the imperative (instruction) form of the verb, and the use of technical language. The children could practise converting statements to instructions, for example:

Statement	Instructions
I stirred the mixture.	Stir the mixture.
I waved my wand.	Wave your wand.

Ask the children to think of occasions when imaginary characters might find a spell handy, and to make notes about what the spell would do, the equipment and materials needed and how to create it. Once they have made the Magic spells book, they can write the spells using their notes to help.

Seven Dwarfs book (pages 23—24)

Talk about the characters in a traditional tale such as *Snow White and the Seven Dwarfs*, and ask the children to think of words that could be used to describe the characters of different dwarfs. Make a list on the board. Explain that each dwarf drawn in the book should have a name label, and the words in the speech bubble should say something about himself (or herself). You could ask the children to think of catchphrases which could be used to advertise a pantomime based on the story, for example, 'Come and hear my amazing yawns,' or 'Learn to grumble from an expert.'

The Ugly Duckling (pages 25—26)

Collect and display pictures of swans and ducks with their young. Discuss the differences between the different birds and between the young and the adults. This could be linked with science work on animal life cycles. Ask the children for words to describe the ducks and swans, and focus on adjectives. Read the story of *The Ugly Duckling* (originally by Hans Christian Andersen) with the class. In the re-telling of the story, the children could concentrate on the use of adjectives in descriptions. They could first make word banks of adjectives, for example:

Ugly Duckling	Swan
awkward	graceful
bedraggled	smooth
brown	white
untidy	sleek

The Frog Prince (pages 27—28)

Give the children copies of the story of The Frog Prince (page 59) for them to read and plan what they want to write in their books. After reading the story, discuss the implications of making promises. Ask the children if they can think of promises they have made which were difficult to keep, or which they made and then wished they hadn't. Encourage them to think about what makes the princess's promise difficult to keep, and what she might be saying to herself at each stage in the story. The children could reveal the princess's character through her 'hidden' thoughts; she might be selfish and unwilling to repay the frog for his help, or she might find it difficult to do as he asks, but convince herself that she owes it to him in return for his help. As an extension activity, the children could write a playscript based on the story, writing the princess's 'hidden thoughts' as asides.

The Three Billy Goats Gruff (pages 29—30)

With the whole class, look at and discuss the use of illustrations in storybooks. Then ask the children to take turns to re-tell parts of this traditional tale, and to think of ways they could change the story, for example, by introducing a new character or event. Their task is to use the model to help them illustrate the story in the best possible way. Extra characters could be drawn on paper, cut out and glued on to the model. The children could discuss their story ideas with a partner or group, and make notes to share with the rest of the class, leading to collaborative story-writing.

Goldilocks and the Three Bears (pages 31—32)

Introduce the activity by showing the children examples of personal organisers. Ask them how a personal organiser is different from a diary and talk about the kinds of things that people might store in a personal organiser: for example, personal information (name, address, phone number), train tickets, shopping lists, reminders, recipes, business cards and notes. Ask the children to take turns to re-tell the story of *Goldilocks and the Three Bears*, and discuss what the bears might keep in their personal organisers. The children could make up the details, based on what they know about the characters. The personal organiser template could also be used for character studies from other stories the children read.

...And it got bigger and bigger
(pages 33—34)
Discuss familiar stories in which something grows, such as *Pinocchio* and *The Enormous Turnip*. Using an enlarged copy of the template, show the children how to make the book and how to draw the growing object, beginning with the top and the bottom and then filling in the middle parts. Encourage the children to make up their own stories in which something grows. They should think about what makes it grow, how it affects the characters in the story, whether the growth needs to be stopped and how it can be stopped. The children can make notes about their ideas before they write their stories.

The Town Mouse and the Country Mouse (pages 35—36)
Read the story of *The Town Mouse and the Country Mouse* with the class. Ask the children which they think is the better place to live — in a town or in the country. They could list the advantages and disadvantages of each on charts, for example:

Town	
Advantages	Disadvantages
Variety of shops nearby	Heavy traffic in rush hour

Country	
Advantages	Disadvantages
Peace and quiet	Not much to do for young people

The children should write on the model where they would prefer to live, supporting their answer with reasons. Using the notes they made on the charts, they could plan a balanced argument about which is the better place to live.

The Hare and the Tortoise (page 37—38)
Tell the story of *The Hare and the Tortoise*, or ask the children to read it (in *Aesop's Fables*, Penguin Classics). Discuss the moral of the story, and any other stories they know with a similar theme, such as *Anansi and the Banana Bird*. You could also discuss any real-life races in which someone with a head start lost to a slower competitor. Play a sports commentary about a race and ask the children how it is different from a report written afterwards: it is in the present, rather then the past, tense; it is not planned (the commentator speaks about the event as it happens); and it is spoken, rather than written. You could discuss the differences between written and unprepared spoken language. The children can present the race as an 'on-the-spot' commentary, moving the puppets as they do so.

Jack and the Beanstalk (pages 39—40)
Discuss the story of *Jack and the Beanstalk*. The children could take turns to re-tell parts of the story. Focus on the beanstalk itself and encourage the children to think of and draw things that might be found on it at different points. They could tell the story of Jack climbing the beanstalk and meeting characters on the way, for example, a caterpillar, a butterfly, a snake and an eagle.

Hansel and Gretel house (pages 41—42)
Ask the children whether they know the story of *Hansel and Gretel*. If they know it, they could take turns to re-tell parts of it; if not, read it to them. Ask them to imagine the witch's cottage, made from sweets. Show them a collection of interesting-looking sweets: for example, twisted barley sugar, liquorice allsorts and boiled sweets. Encourage the children to make accurate drawings of the sweets at a suitable size for the model. They could cut them from thick card, or from several layers of thin card. A twisted barley-sugar or marshmallow stick could be made by rolling strips of thin paper into strands and then twisting several different-coloured strands together.

The Sleeping Beauty (pages 43—44)
Ask the children to take turns to re-tell parts of the story. Discuss the themes of the story: good and evil, and spells cast by an 'evil' character with a grudge being overcome by a 'good' character. The children could identify other stories with these themes. With reference to this and other traditional tales, explain the meaning of 'stock character' and ask the children to identify the stock characters in the story. The children could write on the book their own version of the story, with similar themes and stock 'good' and 'evil' characters.

Pig mask and Wolf mask (pages 45—48)
Organise the children into groups of four and give each group three copies of the Pig mask and one copy of the Wolf mask. Discuss the story of *The Three Little Pigs* and read it together if the children need reminding of it. Help each group to allocate the parts of the wolf and the three pigs. Once they have made the masks, ask them to act out the story. They could also write a playscript of the story (they will need to have read other playscripts first). Discuss the information that needs to be given in a playscript and the way in which it is presented. Help the children to decide if a narrator is needed and what he or she would say. They can find from the story all the information they need to help the actors and director: setting, scenes, props, characters' names, dialogue and actions. The children can record this information on a chart, for example:

Characters: names and details	Props
Scenes: places	Description of places

Once the group has completed the playscript, ask the children to act it out for the class using the masks.

The Little Red Hen (pages 49—50)

Explain to the children that they are going to make a book for younger children, telling a traditional story — *The Little Red Hen*. Give the children copies of the story of The Little Red Hen (page 57) for them to read and plan what they are going to write in their books. Emphasise the repeated language in the story. The children could write their own variation of the story, in which the hen finds something different in the farmyard, such as an apple or a tomato seed.

Little Red Riding Hood Map (pages 51—52)

Talk about the setting and the characters in the story of Little Red Riding Hood. When the children have made the map and drawn on a route, ask them to move a finger along the route as they tell the story and to decide what they can add to the map to make the setting more realistic: for example, trees and houses. Ask them to make a note of all the characters in the story; they could then make cut-out characters which can be placed at different points on the map and moved as they re-tell the story (Little Red Riding Hood, the Wolf, the Woodcutter and Grandmother).

Letter envelope (pages 53—54)

Ask the children to choose a character from a story they have read and to plan a letter to him or her. You may need to revise the conventions of letter-writing. Discuss the different ways in which letters can be begun and ended, and ask the children to choose the one they think is suitable for a letter to the story character they have chosen.

Alternatively, the letter could be used to consider the relationships between two characters, either from the same story or from different ones. The children could write a letter from one character to another about incidents in the stories. They should consider the style of language that the character might use.

Useful contacts

You and your class can find extra ideas, story texts and pictures for the projects in this book by visiting the following websites.

Websites

www.belinus.co.uk/fairytales/Homeextra.htm
  Offers a large collection of fairy tales and fables.
http://childhoodreading.com/
  Features classic children's stories and illustrations.
http://teacher.scholastic.com/writewit/mff/
  Offers resources linked to myths, folk tales and fairy tales, with tips for writing in these genres.
http://english-zone.com/
  Has texts of Aesop's Fables and teachers' resources.
www.storyarts.org
  Includes an online story library and teachers' resources.

www.childrenstory.com/tales/
  Provides texts and illustrations for fairy tales.
www.aesopfables.com
  Features texts of tales by Aesop and other writers.
www.andersenfairytales.com
www.grimmfairytales.com
  Include biographies, learning activities and stories by Hans Christian Andersen and the brothers Grimm respectively.
http://HCA.Gilead.org.il/
  Provides texts of stories by Hans Christian Andersen.
www.artsmia.org/mythology/introduction.html#top
  Provides information on myths from around the world.
www.myths.com/pub/myths/myth.html
  Includes links to related websites.